FROM BROAD-GLASS TO CUT CRYSTAL

PLATE 1.   Cut coloured crystal of today.

FROM
BROAD-GLASS
TO
CUT CRYSTAL

*A History
of the
Stourbridge Glass
Industry*

by

D. R. Guttery

LONDON
LEONARD HILL [BOOKS] LIMITED
NINE EDEN STREET, N.W.1
1956

First published 1956

To
MY WIFE

PRINTED IN GREAT BRITAIN
BY WESTERN PRINTING SERVICES LTD. BRISTOL

CONTENTS

PREFACE

There has been a continuous production of glass in the Stourbridge district now for three hundred and fifty years. Before the
seventeenth century was out, this small area in the Stour Valley
was one of the three chief glass-making centres in the country with
its ten glasshouses making not only the broad-glass of the Lorrainer founders of the industry and bottles but also the new lead
glass. It is true that John Houghton's familiar 1696 list gives
seventeen houses to 'Stowerbridge' ('7 Window glass 5 Bottles
5 Flint green ordinary') but there is little doubt that when a house
produced two of these items, as we know Dennis did for instance,
this was counted twice. The quality of its lead crystal brought the
trade a measure of renown which grew, with the later exploitation
of its brilliancy by cutting, into world fame.

Three booklets by local authors published locally have told
something of the history of the industry; Mr. Francis Buckley
published some notes on the glasshouses during the period 1700–
1830 in the *Transactions of the Society of Glass Technology* while
the same journal has printed a paper by Mr. D. N. Sandilands on
the early years of the trade. All books on English glass have
perforce to give some account; their writers, unacquainted with
the history and geography of the district, depend chiefly and
naturally on an historical summary in the *Victoria County Hospital
of Worcestershire;* unfortunately this article, though assessed by
Mr. W. A. Thorpe as 'a model of exact scholarship', is in many
respects unreliable: it contains errors of fact, misreadings of
documentary evidence and unwarranted assumptions.

No attempt has been made until now to cover the whole period
and tell the story in fuller, if not in the fullest, detail. The account
in the following pages is not offered as a specialist historical study
but is addressed to the reader with interests in fine glass and
English industrial achievement. I have therefore tried not to over-
burden the text with footnotes. For my information I have gone
in all possible cases to the original sources: the parish records of
Oldswinford and Kingswinford; the Court Rolls of the manors of

vii

Oldswinford and Kingswinford, wills, records of Exchequer and Chancery Court Proceedings, Enclosure Act Awards, Canal Surveys, Tithe Maps, documents in the Palfrey Collection, the Library of the Society of Antiquaries and the archives of local firms, the Richardson papers, the Grazebrook genealogies of the Lorrainer families and local newspapers.

Despite the fact that the industry has from its first years been mostly a Staffordshire one and for the last seventy years wholly so, its product bears a Worcestershire trade name, 'Stourbridge Glass'. When the broad-glass makers, originally of Lorraine, settled in the district in the second decade of the seventeenth century, Stourbridge was a busy market town in the parish of Oldswinford, standing on the River Stour, here the boundary between the two counties of Staffordshire and Worcestershire. It had a population of about five hundred people, thriving trades in leather and cloth and a weekly market which drew its custom from wide areas on both sides of the river. Its market and its inns made it the social and business centre of the district; the 'gentlemen-glaziers' bargained in the market and met the men of substance of the neighbourhood in the parlours of its inns. The later establishment of country banks in the town made it the financial centre also; business men from many miles around, scythesmiths, nail-ironmongers, fireclay merchants, colliery owners, clothiers, leather men and glass-makers all used the notes issued by these banks, paying and being paid with them and consequently wherever their works happened to be, headed their bills, 'Stourbridge'. Honeyborne and Batson, predecessors of Stevens and Williams, did this although their works were three miles away in Brierley Hill. So it happened quite naturally that, even though no glass was ever made in Stourbridge town, the glass of the district became known, remained known and is still known as 'Stourbridge Glass'.

Incorporation of the surrounding hamlets into the modern borough brought the sites of the first glasshouse of which we have record, Colemans in the Lye, the Glasshouse Hill house, the only records of which were the foundations discovered about 1864, and the Heath, both in Oldswinford, within the boundaries of the new Stourbridge. To-day the arbitrary geography of the General Post Office decides that all the glass-works of the district (save one) have Stourbridge addresses although all of them are in the Urban Districts of Amblecote and Brierley Hill.

Two public collections of glass have been built up in the district in recent years; they are housed in the Brierley Hill Reference Library and the Council House, Stourbridge. The Brierley Hill Collection was begun in the early nineteen-forties; it consists of more than two hundred pieces, given by the late Mr. W. W. Skidmore Westwood, of Roman, Eastern (Near and Far), Irish, Bohemian, German and Midland English manufacture: twenty-nine pieces presented by Stevens and Williams illustrating the different types of glass made by them during the second half of the nineteenth century and the early years of the twentieth; four very fine cameo vases, two by George Woodall and two by Alphonse Lecheverel, presented by members of the Richardson family, and many pieces of older and modern glass purchased by the Libraries and Arts Committee. This collection is constantly growing by gift and purchase. Librarian H. W. Woodward's wide knowledge and appreciation of fine glass and its literature have enabled the Committee also to build up what must be one of the most complete collections of books, English, American and foreign, on glass and glassmaking in the country.

It was not until after 1951 that Stourbridge made any real attempt to get together a collection of 'Stourbridge Glass' for permanent public exhibition. The Festival of Britain of that year provided an occasion which was seized by local manufacturers and a few private collectors to stage an exhibition of past and present products of the industry. This displayed 163 pieces; half of these (82) came from Stevens and Williams Works' Museum (57), the Brierley Hill Collection (16) and the Wollescote Hall Collection (9), the other half from collectors chief of whom was the late Mr. Benjamin Richardson who sent 44 pieces. The interest aroused by this show resulted in the establishment of the permanent Stourbridge Collection in 1952.

I have been fortunate in the amount of generous help I have been given by the Leverhulme Research Fellowships, by Mr. H. S. Williams-Thomas and Lieut.-Col. R. S. Williams-Thomas of Stevens and Williams, Mr. Tom Jones, Dr. Maskill of Webb Corbett, Mr. W. E. Cook of Stuart's, Mr. H. Collinson of Thomas Webb and Sons; by the Rectors of Kingswinford (Wordsley) and Oldswinford, Mr. F. Bristow, Stourbridge Borough Librarian, Mr. Owen Grazebrook, Mr. F. Kny; Mr. E. Barrington Haynes and Mr. John Northwood; by the following glass-makers: Messrs. W. Evans, J. Nicklin, F. Harper, L. Rides, W. Swingewood and glass-cutter Mr. Joe Harrop, and by Miss B. E. Hayward. Alderman H. E. Palfrey's unique collection of documents has been open to me at all times; Mr. Arthur Arrowsmith made special journeys to Amblecote to draw Dennis House and the old Glass-house Cone at Hollowsend, and my brother, Mr. W. A. Guttery, has worked wonders on some old photographs for me.

I am particularly indebted to two friends, Mr. Geoffrey W. Beard and Mr. H. W. Woodward, who have both helped me on many occasions on many matters in many ways.

To all I offer my very sincere thanks.

AMBLECOTE, 1955   D. R. GUTTERY

LIST OF ILLUSTRATIONS

Chapter 1

PAUL TYZACK
THE FIRST STOURBRIDGE GLASS-MAKER

When young Paul Tyzack, now master of the art, feat and mystery of broad-glass making, set out in the early years of the seventeenth century from a glass-house in Bishops Wood, Eccleshall, for the Stour Valley, with his belongings slung over his pony's back and his tools (exact counterparts of those used by the glass-makers of to-day) over his shoulder and stuck in his belt, he was following a craft and family tradition, for the Tyzacks had for many generations all been broad-glass makers and had followed the woods. He was not to know that this short journey was to break that tradition, that it was the journey to end all journeys for ever.

Noble though the Tyzacks were, du Thisacs, *gentilshommes verriers*, they had been tramps from the early fifteenth century when they had left the woods of Bohemia and begun their long trek to Darney Forest in the Vosges. It was fuel that dictated their movements and decided the sites of their furnaces; when their hungry fires had burned through one wood they moved to another. The Vosges forests promised an inexhaustible supply of the cleft billets they threw into their furnaces, not only for themselves, but also for the Henzeys (de Hennezel) and the Titterys (de Thiétry), their close kinsmen and, like them, gentlemen, tramps, broad-glass makers.

For nearly two hundred years, the men of these families using the crude raw materials of this forest country and the blown and slit-cylinder method, described by Theophilus in the eleventh century, but processing their metal according to some secret formula handed down from father to son and preserved by the strictest of protective oaths, had been producing the best window-glass obtainable.

It was not a failure of fuel, however, in Lorraine but the beguilement of a nine-year contract offered them by an Antwerp speculator, Jean Carré (with, maybe, fear of persecution in the

1

troubled religious world of the continent enhancing this) which brought members of these families into England in 1568.

The times were not propitious; a fuel crisis was rapidly developing here and nowhere were its stringencies more acute than in the Sussex to which they were brought to work; the Weald had long been our chief iron-producing district and the native iron-workers naturally did not welcome claims on a quickly disappearing source of fuel especially as these came from foreigners; the facts that these glass-makers could use wood as wood whereas they themselves had to bear the cost and trouble of charring it first, that the outlanders were mobile and could carry their craft so easily to their fuel, that they were over-jealous of their secret techniques and, despite the contrary terms of the contract to which they had subscribed their outlandish names, would not teach Englishmen their trade, made their presence still more obnoxious to the ironworkers. However, the arson that was practised and the murder that was threatened against them did not prevent the Lorrainers from fulfilling their contract. But, so soon as this had been worked out, most of them left the district (only a few Henzeys remaining until about 1610), not, as most earlier foreign glass-makers had done, to return home. They had come to England to stay; so they trekked westwards in search of fresh woods unhaunted by rival furnacemen; west to Hampshire, to Somerset, Gloucester and the Forest of Dean, then northwards up the valley of the busy Severn, one of the busiest rivers in Europe, into the heart of England where they were destined to stay.[1]

By 1585, the year in which official attention seems first to have been given to the disproportionate toll glass-makers were taking of our timber supplies as they blazed their trail through the country, Tyzacks and Henzeys had already set up furnaces in Bishops Wood in Eccleshall parish on the Salop border of Staffordshire, while another Henzey was making his broad-glass in Bagots Park at Blithfield.[2] This official attention resulted in the drawing up of a Bill 'against the making of glass by strangers and outlandish men and for the preservation of woods spoiled by glass-houses'. This Bill, though passed through all its stages, never received the Royal assent to become an Act, the Committee chosen to sit on it 'being such as sold woods to the Frenchmen', or so claimed a cynical Englishman whose fiery indignation was fanned

[1] Buckholt, nr. Salisbury 1576–79; Newent, 1599–1601; Eccleshall, 1584–1601; Cheswardine, 1601–13.
[2] Ambrose Henzey making broad-glass at 18s. the case for Richard Bagot.

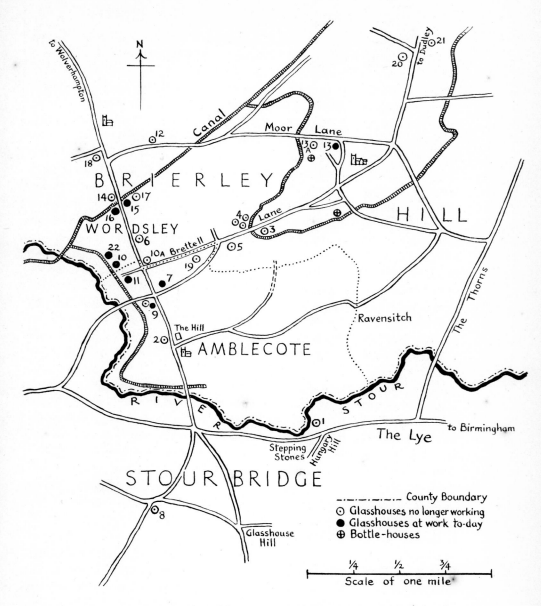

PLATE 2.   Map showing sites of glass-houses.

The glass-houses are numbered in the order of their building.

1.	Colemans.	12.	Dob Hill.
2.	Holloway End.	13.	Moor Lane (13a. Original site)
3.	Brettell.	14.	Bradley's I.
4.	Bague's.	15.	Red House.
5.	Hawbush.	16.	White House.
6.	Audnam.	17.	The Albert.
7.	Dennis.	18.	Kinver Street.
8.	The Heath.	19.	Haden's.
9.	Coalbournbrook.	20.	The Wallows.
10.	The Dial (10a. Original site).	21.	Round Oak.
11.	Platts.	22.	The new Audnam.

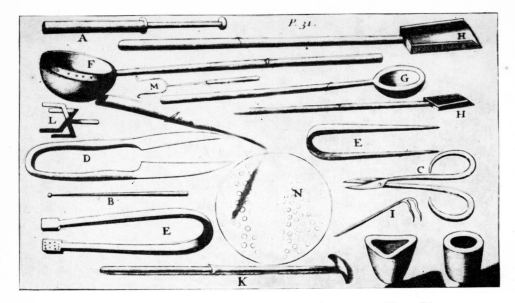

PLATE 3. Set of glassmaker's tools, seventeenth century. (From Blancourt's *Art of Glass*.)

A.   The hollow Pipe serves to blow the Glass.

B.   The Rod . . . to take up the Glass after it is blown, and cut off the former.

C.   The Shears.

D.   The Shears . . . to shape the great Glasses.

E.   This Instrument serves to finish the Work.

F.   The great Ladle . . . to take out the Metal of the great Pot and put it into the little ones for the Work-men.

G.   The little Ladle . . . this serves for skiming the Metal.

H.   The great and little Shovels serve only to take up the great Glasses.

I.   The hooked Fork serves to stir the matter in the Pots.

K.   The Rake to move about the Fritt in the first Oven.

L.   This instrument is for making Chamber-pots.

M.   The Fork to carry the Glass-works into the upper Oven to cool them.

N.   The great Ladle serves to take off the Alkalick salt.

by the obstinate refusal of these outlanders to teach Englishmen their trade despite contractual promises to do so.[1]

But glass-makers and metalworkers were by no means the only spoilers of the woods: brewers, brickmakers, limeburners, bakers, potters and salters, the manufacturers of tar, starch, sugar and gunpowder were all consuming (and necessarily in the absence of any other practicable fuel) the country's timber. There was only one alternative to industrial collapse in the near future—the use of some other fuel, and a feverish experimental search for this had already been in progress for some years. Obviously that fuel was sooner or later to be the pit-coal with which so many parts of the country abounded. 'Ingenious gentlemen' abounded, too, of the type who were later to found the Royal Society, who were experimenting with this, but it proved a very intractable subject, particularly because of its many and various impurities which in different ways spoiled the product.

One of the most earnest of these experimenters (driven as much by financial stringency as by scientific curiosity and industrial necessity) was Lord Dudley, beneath whose estates in south-west Staffordshire lay the richest deposits of coal in the country. These estates had already been sadly deforested by his smiths so that he was in almost desperate need of charcoal, a need which had been intensified by his erection of one of the new blast-furnaces[2] near the Stour in his Kingswinford manor, a furnace which consumed much more charcoal than his old bloomeries had done. He tried pit-coal instead of charcoal and spoiled his iron; whatever trial he made he failed; at the same time his smiths found that they could use it in their forge hearths.

Experiments in other industries achieved more success; the glass-makers solved their problem; hitherto their pots had stood open in the furnace; by covering the pots they prevented any contamination of their metal by the smoke and fumes from the new fuel. Their success resulted in a patent (carrying with it the trade monopoly) being granted in 1610 to Sir William Slingsby and his associates for melting glass, copper, brass, tin, &c. with pit-coal. A year later Sir Edward Zouche obtained one for glass alone, 'all manner of glasses'; amended in 1613, this Zouche

[1] This was a common complaint heard everywhere, in Paris, Ireland, Virginia as well as in England, against the foreign glass-makers.

[2] The blast-furnace had been introduced into the Midlands by Lord Paget at Cannock; he had been followed by yeoman Parkes at Wednesbury and he by Lord Dudley whose furnace was built in the Saltwells Wood, near the Mousesweet Brook.

patent covered 'drinking glasses, broad-glass and other glasses and glasswork'.

Broad-glass—that is, window-glass made by the special Lorrainer technique as opposed to the Norman glass-makers' Crown-glass.[1] The grant of this patent meant that only the Tyzacks, the Henzeys and Titterys, could make window-glass henceforth with pit-coal and this only under licence from Sir Edward Zouche.

Where were these masters of this craft at the time? An entry in the Kingswinford Parish Register partially answers this question:

'April 26, 1612, John Tysacke the sonne of Paule Tysacke and Bridgett his wife was bapt.'

Paul's journey from Eccleshall had brought him to Lord Dudley's Kingswinford and here he seems to have worked quietly for a year or two, probably experimenting with the new fuel and adapting his pots to the new conditions. Why did he come here? To settle where pit-coal[2] was easily available? But Kingswinford was not the only district in Staffordshire where coal was to be got. Was glass already being made here? Using this coal as fuel? It is probable that it was.

Coal was certainly being used with complete success by glass-makers by 1615, for in that year a Royal Proclamation forbade further use of 'Timber, or wood, or any Fewell made of Timber or wood' in their furnaces. In that same year Admiral Sir Robert Mansell, the man who was destined to organize the glass industry on a national basis and control it for the next forty years, joined Zouche and his partners and plunged at once into his industrial career, settling John Squire, who had worked at Eccleshall and Cheswardine, and Jacob Henzey in a glass-house at Wollaton, Nottingham.[3] By 1618, Mansell had bought out all his partners and held the monopoly alone, although this was not officially recognized until 1623 when he had to fight hard to retain it.

So many ills had arisen from abuses of the monopoly system that public protest had resulted in a 'Statute of Monopolies' which declared that from 1624 all monopolies 'are and shall be utterly void and of none effect'; only such as were based on genuinely new inventions were henceforth to be considered. There were two

---

[1] Crown-glass was made by spinning a disc of metal, trundling it like a mop.   [2] 'Pit-coal' to distinguish it from char-coal.

[3] On land leased from Sir Percival Willoughby who supplied the coal. One of the witnesses to this indenture was James Howell, a young man of twenty-one, who became Mansell's 'traveller'. He wrote the famous *Familiar Letters* which contain so much of interest concerning glass-making here and on the Continent.

significant exemptions: Mansell's by Section XIII while Section XIV expressly allowed Lord Dudley's 'grant concerning the melting of iron'. Lord Dudley (really his bastard son Dud Dudley) had succeeded in sufficient measure in using pit-coal to be granted an iron monopoly in 1622.

Despite this official reprieve, Mansell's monopoly was very strongly attacked in 1624 in the 'Honorable Assembly of the Commons' and one of its chief critics was Lord Dudley himself. Lord Dudley made a claim which, whatever its moment to him at the time, is of great importance to the history of glassmaking; it was that the patent (Zouche's) on which Mansell's monopoly was based should not have been granted since the invention was not new:

'two yeares before this pretence of a new invention, or any Patent granted there was Glasse made with Coale upon his ground by native Glasse-makers'.

'Upon his ground', that is, on one of his estates in the south-west corner of Staffordshire; almost certainly that meant Kingswinford for it was in this manor that he was carrying on his industrial pursuits.

No record remains of these English glass-makers, no names, no sites, unless later houses were built on them, but Dud Dudley repeated his father's claim in his book *Metallum Martis* and says they worked near to his dwelling-house; this was Green Lodge, near Greensforge in the north-west corner of Kingswinford.[1]

It was probably news of this enterprise which brought Paul Tyzack into Kingswinford at some time before April 1612 when his first child was christened there. Once here he discovered that in addition to an abundance of pit-coal there was also mined a very useful clay for making pots, in fact, the best clay he had ever used and enough of both to satisfy any demand.

The native glass-makers were probably making green vessels and phials, but what about window-glass? If there was none made here it was imported, for in the early years of the seventeenth century, the first for which the Churchwardens' Accounts of Oldswinford are preserved, in 1604–5 and 1605–6, are items of expenditure 'for glasyng the Churche Wyndowes'.[2]

---

[1] In the sixteen-forties Dud Dudley was described as of the Parish of Wombourne. It is interesting that Wombourne Church is one of the few dedicated to St. Benedict Biscop, the patron saint of glass-makers.

[2] Was Paul making this? We do not know where else he was at this time. Maybe it was brought from Eccleshall; in 1604–5 there is an item 'for getting of same' (that is, the glass) and one 'for carriage'; but there is no such item in 1605–6.

It was to make window-glass, broad-glass, to practise his traditional craft, that Paul Tyzack settled here. Where and when he blew his first cylinder we do not know. A volume of MSS. in Birmingham Reference Library contains the Daybook of a Lichfield attorney practising at this time; this gives lists of documents he prepared for his clients between June 1613 and October 1621; among these clients were persons from the Lye, Amblecote and Stourbridge. Against the date June 1618 appears this item:

'Mrs. Adenbrooke has leases for Paul Tysaac and—'

Mrs. Addenbrook's husband had just died, Henry Addenbrook of the Lye,[1] who had worked coal and clay there and had two mills on the Stour, one of which 'Stanborne Mylle'[2] has given us the modern district name of Stambermill. This lease of 1618 may have been a confirmation of an earlier one made to Paul by Henry Addenbrook. An entry in the Oldswinford Court Rolls suggests that Paul was a tenant of land in Oldswinford in 1616;[3] another entry with slighter implication, an ordinance forbidding anyone to burn bracken within the manor under a heavy penalty, suggests the activities of some glass-makers as early as 1612, for green bracken was the source of the early glass-makers' potash.

By 1618, at least, he was in possession of a 'leasowe' called Colemans, a significant name: both coal and clay lay at their different depths under it. He did not live on the ground but on the opposite bank of the Stour, on land which was part of Ravensitch Coppice in the Parish of Kingswinford.[4] Between Colemans and Ravensitch a bridge, for the upkeep of which he was responsible, crossed the stream. Some short distance away stepping stones provided an alternative crossing. Later on, his son-in-law, Paul Henzey, was to rent a piece of land adjoining Colemans and called 'Stepping Stones'[5] another name extant to-day.

On Colemans Paul Tyzack built the first glass-house of which we have any record in the Stourbridge district; it stood just over a mile from the Town Hall in the centre of the busy market town. What we know of the Lorrainers' houses suggests that it was

---

[1] In the daybook: 'Henricus Adenbrooke de Lee in Com Wigorn gen.'

[2] Mentioned in the Inventory to his will, proved 9 June 1618.

[3] He was fined because his maidservant had broken into the lord's pound and retrieved some straying cattle of Paul's which had been impounded.

[4] His children were christened at Kingswinford Church and he and his wife were buried there.

[5] Paul probably got the stone for his furnace from 'Stepping Stones'; the following two items appear in the Churchwardens' Accounts for 1604–5:

'Itm for getting of a loade of stone   vjd.
Itm for cariage from steping stones   ijs.'

about forty feet square, of timber with a shingled roof, the ridge some thirty-six feet high, the square furnace of freestone, the 'ovens' of that excellent clay[1] he could dig on his own ground. Such are the details of a Lorraine house built in southern Ireland for Davy the Frenchman at the same time as Colemans; the cost of building was £8 for the house and £4 'and 12 pence' for the ovens.[2]

Before Colemans was built other Lorrainers had, probably on the strength of Paul's news, come into the district; and 1615, the year of the Proclamation forbidding their use of wood fuel, saw the beginning of an invasion by Lorrainers and other 'outlandish glassmakers' which was to continue without interruption, despite the Civil War, for the next fifty years and was to bring here some of the most famous of all, Dagnias, Rachettis, Visitalias.

The Lorrainers worked in teams of three; who were Paul's two partners? The two earliest foreign glass-makers mentioned in the Oldswinford Parish Register were Francis Conculyn in 1613 and 'Danyell Bunger' who was buried in 1615; in the Kingswinford Register appears James Legre in 1617. Legre had been with Paul at Eccleshall and had married his sister there while Paul's brother Zacharias is mentioned in 1620. It is likely that these two with Paul made up the first Stourbridge 'chair', gaffer, blower and gatherer.

England was no longer a strange land to the Lorrainers; the fifty years they had spent here had been long enough for them to shed most of their outlandishness. Paul's gentility and prosperity were soon recognized; by 1617 he was 'Mr. Paul Tyzack' in the Kingswinford register and a little later 'Paul Tyzack. gent.' in the Oldswinford Court Rolls. At first, Colemans supplied a purely local market[3] with its window-glass at 22s. 6d. a case; the Oldswinford Churchwardens' Accounts suggest it was 6½d. a foot, so that it was a costly commodity.[4] Paul worked forty weeks in the

[1] Mansell was soon bringing this clay (now known as 'Stourbridge Fireclay' but in these early days as 'Amblecote Glasshouse Pot Clay') into general use; until he found the cost and difficulties of transport too great, he was sending it as far as to Newcastle upon Tyne.

[2] Paul Tyzack, Junior, claimed that after its destruction by fire in 1658 it cost him £200 to rebuild Colemans.

[3] On 30 March 1636 at the Manorial Court held in the Town Hall, Stourbridge, a man was fined 2s. 6d. for assaulting a 'crate-carrier'; the crate probably contained window-glass and was carried on the back.

In 1713 Captain Philip Roche, a Dublin glass-maker, left £5 'to those who cry about glasses and travel into the country to sell glass'.

[4] Costs given are 6s. 6d., 6s. 6d., 10s. 10d., 4s. 4d., etc. The costliness of this glass may be judged from the fact that money then was something about twenty times its present value.

7

year and his normal weekly output was eighteen cases. He was paying an annual rent of £30 and his licence from Sir Robert Mansell cost him £60.

The provision of raw materials was not difficult; he was allowed by the terms of his lease to use as much of the coal and clay on his land as he needed; he had probably some agreement with the lord of the manor to cut green bracken from the wastes for his potash and prohibit others from cutting it for bedding for their animals until the autumn; he used one of the local sands, not from his own grounds it seems, for on occasion he was presented and fined at the Court Baron for tipping it 'in the King's Highway leading from the Lye to Old Swinford to the harm of the vill and the King's subjects'.

At some time during Paul's tenancy Colemans changed hands and John Lyddiat of Wollaston Hall[1] became his new landlord. He was a violent man, a throwback to the turbulent pre-Tudor days, and was presented at Courts Baron for almost every kind of social misdemeanour.[2] However, despite trouble that was constantly brewing, Paul remained at Colemans and his son, Paul, married Lyddiat's daughter, Joyce.

Paul's nephew Zacharias gave him more trouble. When Zacharias, senior, Paul's brother and partner died, Paul took the boy under his charge and taught him the family trade: his seven years' apprenticeship completed, he remained as a master workman with his uncle, receiving a gaffer's wage of 30s. a week for two years, when he left his uncle to work for Anne Tittery, widow of Daniel, at her Amblecote house. He married, quarrelled with his father-in-law, killed the family mare in a rage and ran back to his uncle for shelter at Colemans, from which time on he remained to work with Paul and afterwards with Paul junior.

Paul lived comfortably and reared a family of six children; three of his four daughters (token of his now being deeply rooted in this country) married Englishmen; the fourth, Ann, followed the Lorrainers' tradition of intermarriage, his only child to do so; both his sons married Englishwomen. Ann became the wife of Paul Henzey. Evidence given in a lawsuit spoke of Paul senior as having been 'always reputed an honest and just-dealing person'.

It was probably preoccupation with his craft which caused that neglect of certain civic responsibilities for which he was presented

---

[1] Lyddiat was a scythesmith with mills at Greensforge and Himley.

[2] His offences including assaulting the constable, wounding several persons, filling in his tenants' wells, stopping their rights of way, etc.

PLATE 4. Workman's Card at Richardson's about 1850.

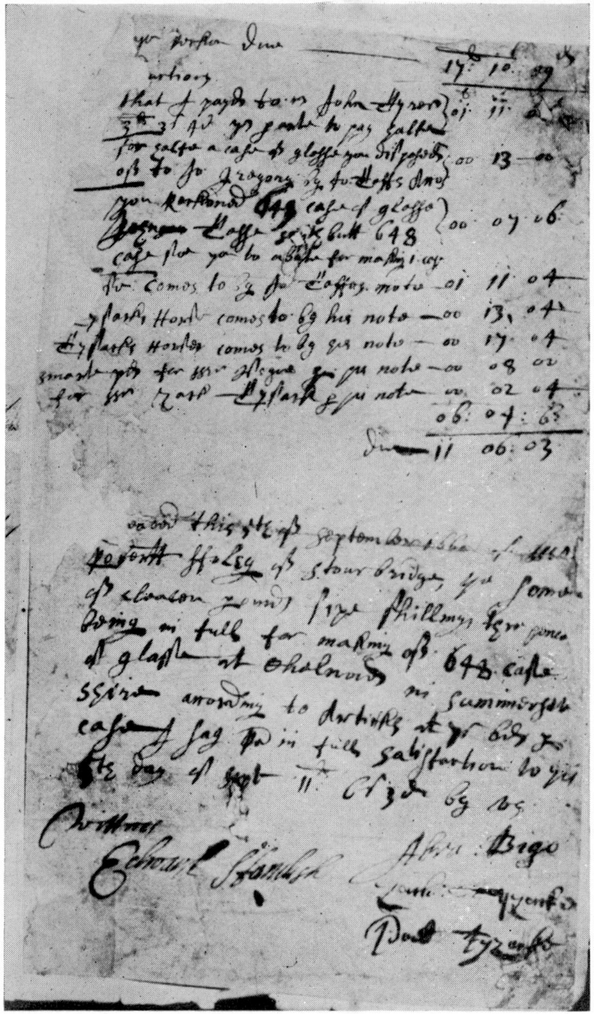

PLATE 5. Receipt for payment for work done by the Coleman's chair for Robert Foley at Chelwood, 1660.' Signed by Abraham Bigo, Zachariah Tyzacke and Paul Tyzacke.

Transcription :

	£	s	d
yor porsion due	17:	10:	09
(Ded)uctions			
that I payd to mr John Tyrer } 3£ 3s 4d yr parte to pay halfe }	01:	11:	08
for halfe a case of glasse you disposed } of to Jo Gregory by Jo Toses Acco }	00:	13:	00
you Reckoned 649 case of glasse John Tosse seyth butt 648 case soe you to abate for making 1 case	00:	07:	06
. . . (hor)se comes to by Jo Tosses note	01:	11:	04
. . . (T)ysacks Horse comes to by his note	00:	13:	04
. . Tysacks Horse comes to by his note	00:	17:	04
Smarte pd for Mr Bigoe per his note	00:	08:	00
for Mr Zach Tysack per his note	00:	02:	04
	06:	04:	6
due	11:	06:	03

(Rec)eaved this 5th of September 1660 of Mr Robertt ffoley of Stourbridge ye some of eleaven pounds sixe shillings thre pence being in full for making of 648 case of glasse at Chelwood in Summersett shire according to Articles at 7s 6d per case I say pd in full satisfaction to — 5th day of Sept 11£: 6s 3d by us
Wittnes
 Edward Standish

Abra : Bigo
Zach : Tyzacke
Paul Tyzacke

From the Palfrey Collection.

and fined at the Manorial Court, but for nothing more serious than his neglecting to repair his bridge over the Stour, obstructing the highway with his sand or a tree he had felled. Since glassmakers then worked the same six-hour shift as their successors were to do for three hundred years, six hours on, six hours off, it must have been difficult for him to find time for such outside jobs.[1] In 1655, after more than forty years' work in this district, Paul retired, handing over Colemans to his second son, Paul, who agreed to pay him an annuity of £40.[2]

For his remaining ten years Paul lived in his house in Ravensitch Coppice with his favourite son-in-law Paul Henzey, who had taken the property over in the previous year. Paul Henzey was a good family man, whose widowed mother, an Englishwoman (Joan Brettell), was a few years later to leave him all she had with this comment, 'and all I have is too little for him'. With Paul and Ann Henzey and their seven children, the old man lived happily in the Coppice, fitting shelter for a Tyzack whose traditional craft had been woodland born. From Ravensitch he watched over his son's varying fortunes at Colemans. His vacant place there was taken over by the much younger Abraham Bigo (Bigault) whose father had been working at Cheswardine[3] but had obtained a licence from Mansell in 1618 to make glass in the Isle of Purbeck; this venture failed and he went to Ireland. Young Zacharias was now at Colemans, too.

In 1658, a fire completely destroyed the glass-house (John Lyddiat later accused his son-in-law of having set fire to it). Paul had not as yet sufficient capital to rebuild and his father-in-law refused to help. In order presumably to raise enough to rebuild Colemans, Paul entered into a contract with Robert Foley, the now wealthy Midlands ironmaster and government contractor; the Lorrainers had a London warehouse on the upper floor of Foley's, in Leadenhall Street. By the terms of the contract Paul, Zacharias and Bigo were to make broad-glass at Chelwood[4] in Somerset, Foley to pay them 7s. 6d. a case.[5] He was selling this at 26s. a case, probably at Bristol, where he had premises, for the

[1] This six-hour shift was not generally abandoned until just before the Second World War.

[2] Two thirds of a gaffer's wages at the time; gaffer's were paid 30s. a week, blowers 20s. and gatherers 10s. and worked usually forty weeks in the year; for to-day's values turn these shillings into £'s.

[3] Cheswardine, near Eccleshall, but in Shropshire.

[4] 'Chellwood' appears in John Houghton's 1696 list as one of three glasshouses in Somerset making bottles and window-glass.

[5] Davy the Frenchman was paid 3s. a case in the Irish house in 1620.

coastwise trade to London. Seven shillings and sixpence a case meant that the partners between them were earning £6 15s. a week for a normal week's output.[1]

By March 1661, they were all back at Colemans; Paul took out a fresh lease for twelve years and rebuilt the glass-house at a cost of £200. This figure, Paul's own (Lyddiat later said it cost his son-in-law no more than £90), suggests that the new house was built of stone or brick in place of timber. Three years later, Paul entered into a new contract with Foley, who had by this time risen still higher in the commercial world and was now official Ironmonger to the Royal Navy; this contract was arranged by Joshua Henzey the Second who was then marketing the whole of the window-glass made in the Stourbridge district. Paul engaged to supply 1600 cases a year for three years at 20s. a case. He had barely begun to work on this when Lyddiat brought an action of ejectment against him. The result of this case is unknown but in 1670 the same three partners were at work at Withymoor, on the Staffordshire side of the Stour in Amblecote, under a landlord who, according to the evidence in the case, had held a mortgage on Colemans.

By that time Paul senior had been dead five years. He had little estate to leave. Pioneering costs, dowries for his four daughters, ten years of retirement and an innate generosity had eaten deeply into his substance. Though his fortune in money was a meagre £25, he spread this over no less than twenty-two bequests; first of these was £12 to be divided equally among his seven Henzey grandchildren, whose childhood had been spent under his benign eye; three of the bequests were sixpences. One debt, of £40, was owing to him. He made Paul Henzey his sole executor.

When Paul died, the Stourbridge glass industry of which he had laid the foundation stone at Colemans was flourishing; its past achievement and future promise were sufficient to have already attracted such masters of the craft as the Rachettis[2] and the Visitalias to work here and such local men as Thomas Rogers to take an active interest in it. The Henzeys had houses in Amblecote and Brettell (Brierley Hill), while the Bagues[3] also had one in Brettell.

[1] In the Palfrey Collection is part of an account statement concerning this contract, probably the earliest document extant concerning Stourbridge glass.

[2] 'Ceazer Rackett' married Paul's granddaughter Merriall, at Kingswinford in 1665.

[3] Said by most writers on the subject to be the same family as the Bigoes; they were not.

The first Paul Tyzack occupies a most important place in the history of English glass-making; his importance in that of Stourbridge glass-making is even greater. He may have been the first glass-maker ever to have brought the use of pit-coal as the glass-makers' fuel to complete success: he was certainly the first to do so in the Stourbridge area; indeed, his is the first recorded name of any glass-maker using any kind of fuel here. If the glass used in Oldswinford church windows in 1604 came from outside the area, it may have come from Eccleshall and have been made there by the Tyzacks, although the last parish register record of a Tyzack there is in 1602. Between that date and 1612 when Paul's son was christened at Kingswinford there is no record known of him anywhere. But in that eleven-year interim Paul would be making window-glass somewhere near; the evidence of the Dudleys, our knowledge of the experiments with pit-coal being made here in the early years of the seventeenth century and Paul's being certainly settled here by 1612, strengthen the suggestion that he came here to survey the prospects and probably to carry on experiments himself.

His success at Colemans put an end to the Lorrainer nomad tradition and fixed for ever the site of a world-famous industry. Paul Tyzack achieved that success as a pioneer in a foreign country without the substantial financial backing which English glassmen were getting. If only one of the names of the early foreign glass-makers here was to survive into English industry to-day it is fitting that this name should be his. About a mile downstream from the site of Colemans stands to-day one of the works belonging to Nash-Brades-Tyzack.

11

Chapter 2

THE FIRST HENZEYS

Those members of the gentlemen-glazier families from Lorraine who settled on the South Staffordshire coalfield after the Proclamation of 1615 and the pioneer Paul Tyzack's proof of the district's suitability for the practice of their craft, set up their furnaces in the two adjoining Swinford parishes, Old Swinford and Kings Swinford. Oldswinford was a Worcestershire parish which here jumped the Stour, the county boundary, to include the Staffordshire manor of Amblecote. Kings Swinford was wholly in Staffordshire. Only in one very small area of the coalfield along the boundary between the two Swinfords is the famous fireclay[1] mined; it was there the Lorrainers built their glass-houses.

The year 1615 was a most important one in the history of English glass-making; it was the year of the Royal Proclamation which not only forced pit-coal on to the glass-makers, but, by forbidding at the same time the importation of foreign glass, gave the English industry a challenge and an opportunity. In this same year Sir Robert Mansell,[2] taking up the challenge, began that career in glass-making which was to organize the industry as a national concern. On 8 December 1615, he signed an agreement with Sir Percival Willoughby[3] to take over a glass-house at Wollaton, Nottingham; two men are named as being in occupation of this, Jacob Henzey and John Squire, 'Glassmakers'.

On the following day, according to an entry in the Oldswinford Parish Register

'1615 Dec 9 Paule sonne of Jacob Henzie baptd.'

[1] This fireclay was first mined in Amblecote and for long was known as 'Amblecote Glasshouse Pot Clay'; now it is 'Stourbridge Fireclay'.

[2] In 1620 the Venetian Ambassador in London reported home: 'General Mansfilt is a bold ardent and very ambitious man.'

[3] Willoughby was working coalpits on his estate there; a really 'ingenious' gentleman, ironmaster, too, and grower of woad to foster a dye industry. John Squire had been at Eccleshall with the Henzeys; he had married a Margaret Evans there; five of their children were christened at Cheswardine (1601–12); the marriage entry gives his wife's father's name as 'Yeaven Aprice'. Surely this is 'Evan ap-Rhys' and Welsh, not French, as so many writers claim. 'Squire' is a name still connected with glass here; one Squire is a glasshouse-pot maker to-day in Amblecote.

By courtesy of Stuart & Sons Ltd.

PLATE 6.   The Glass-maker

PLATE 7. 'The Potmaker'

This is the first appearance in a local record of the name which was to dominate glass here until the third Joshua Henzey died in 1737. Between that date, 1615 and 1630, seven Henzey families are mentioned in the registers of the Swinfords.

On that serial journey from the Weald to this district, which lasted for more than thirty years, the Lorrainers and their foreign associates and fellow-craftsmen had not moved like a caravan in a compact body; only the general direction was common to all. Some, including Henzeys, probably came directly north from Buckholt via Warwickshire, not like the others by the Severn Valley. Some Becke or Beckes settled at Alcester; John Henzey married Mary Becke[1] of that town in the sixteen-forties. In 1585, Ambrose Henzey was making glass at Blithfield near Rugeley, a further point on the same route, under the industrial patronage and with the financial backing of Richard Bagot. By the same year other Henzeys, by the Severn route, had reached Eccleshall.

It is very likely that young James Howell,[2] Mansell's manager, came into the Midlands to help and direct the Lorrainers' move to the coalfields, some, as we have seen, to Nottingham, some to Newcastle upon Tyne and others to the Stourbridge district. The Nottingham venture did not last long; in the two other districts the industry quickly prospered and for some years a great deal of both personal and business traffic passed between them. In both it was the Henzeys who took the lead. The Henzey who assumed that leadership here was the first of the three Joshuas.

The names of the three earliest glass-houses in the Stourbridge district are often mentioned together in what records are extant: these are Colemans, the Hooe and Brettell. Built in that order they stood at the three corners of a roughly equilateral triangle with a side of about three-quarters of a mile, Colemans in the Lye by the Stour on the Stourbridge–Birmingham road, the Hooe in Amblecote on the Stourbridge–Wolverhampton road and Brettell in Brettell,[3] one of the 'liberties' of the Kingswinford

[1] Antony Becku had been Jean Carré's original partner.
[2] James Howell was one of the witnesses to the Willoughby-Mansell agreement 1615.
[3] There is a good deal of confusion about the name 'Brettell'; a family named Brettell lived in a district called Brettell; it would seem that the family took its name from the district. However, originally the family name seems to have been Bredhill or Bredhull (fourteenth century) while the district name was Bryt Hill (appearing so in record of a Star Chamber case in the fifteenth century). Local pronunciation has preserved this in spite of modern spelling; it is usually 'Brittle Lane'; on some early maps, too, it appears so or as 'Britwell'. From Kingswinford Parish Register—'1693 Mar 10 John Brittel of Brittel was buried'.

parish, near the Stourbridge–Dudley road. Colemans was pioneer Paul Tyzack's; the name of the Hooe suggests that it was built by one of the du Houx family; Brettell was the first Henzey glasshouse here. Members of the du Houx family had tramped with the other Lorrainers from Sussex; they are recorded in Gloucestershire where they set up a furnace without paying a licence and so fell foul of the fearsome Sir Jerome Bowes, monopolist at the time, who compelled them to close it; then at Cheswardine. Records of them here are very few: one married a Tyzack in 1623, Absalom de Hoo was being sued for debt in 1657, according to the Kingswinford Court Rolls; Thomas Hoo witnessed the third Joshua Henzey's will in 1738. The du Houx were not traditional broad-glass makers, but makers of vessels. They seem not to have remained here to work for long; further records of them are at Market Drayton, Hyde in Cheshire and then in London.[1] It is probable that their house was taken over first by the Henzeys and then by the Titterys.

Two Henzey brothers, Edward and Peregrine, were here immediately after 1615; among the family papers is a record of their selling their lands in France in 1620 which refers to them as of 'Amblecote au comté de Stratford'. In the next year Edward died; in his will he had named Peregrine, 'Perrigrin Hensey my brother', and 'Joshua Hensey my kinsman' as overseers. This suggests that these three formed the first Henzey 'chair' here. Joshua was to become the leading local figure in the glass industry.

He had just attained his majority but had already been married for three years and to an Englishwoman; the wedding had taken place at Kingswinford church in 1618. His bride, Joan Brettell, was the red-haired daughter of one of the oldest and most substantial families in the parish; despite her being ten years older than her youthful bridegroom, her acceptance of this foreigner is a significant token of the easy entrance the Lorrainers had been able to make into the social life of the district; further evidence of this is in the fact that one of Joan's brothers married a Maria Henzey who may have been Joshua's sister. Joan's wedding seems to have been (and necessarily) a hurried affair, for just six days after its solemnization she brought another Henzey into the world, a son, Ananias, and, so tradition says, a first instalment of that red hair which was her most lasting contribution to the Henzey family.

[1] Advertisement in *London Gazette* 7 August 1693: 'Mr. Isaac Dehew, at the Adam & Eve, Ratcliff highway making Looking Glasse, Crown Glass, Bottles, Chymical Glass all at one furnace.'

In this father-son business of broad-glass making the Henzey boys would spend many of their out-of-school hours in the family glass-house and quickly attain some proficiency in the craft. There is no record of Joshua's father, Ananias, having been in this district so the boy probably worked and mastered the 'art feat and mystery' with his uncles, Edward and Peregrine.

By 1630 he was buying land in Brettell, coal-bearing land, and it was on this that he built his glass-house, the house in which, though he had other trade interests in Ireland and London, he was to work all his life. The actual site of this first Henzey glass-house is not definitely known; the liberty of Brettell lay about the southern and western slopes of Brierley Hill (before the township developed) reaching the Delph on one side and Moor Lane on the other and stretching westwards to the Amblecote and Wordsley borders. The Dudley–Stourbridge road, here now called Brettell Lane, roughly bisects the area. Entries in the Kingswinford Court Rolls indicate that Joshua's lands were on the south side of that road and touched it between Silver End and the site of George King-Harrison's brickworks. Since so many of the later glass-houses were built on the sites of older ones and since these sites always adjoined a main road it is highly probable that Wheeley's glass-house was built on the site of Joshua's. Wheeley's, we know, stood on the land now covered by Brettell Lane Railway Station.

Prosperity came in good measure and quickly to Joshua and he became something of a public figure. Living in Kingswinford he had his children christened at St. Mary's Church, but the church and civic activities he undertook seem to have been confined to the neighbouring parish of Oldswinford to which (Amblecote) he had first come. In 1638 he was one of the Overseers of the Poor for Amblecote; in 1643–4 and again in 1644–5 he was Church Warden; in the following year he was appointed a sidesman.[1] By 1651, at least, he was one of the governors of the 'free Grammar School of King Edward the Sixth situate in Stourbridge', the school his boys would almost certainly attend. His being elected to these offices reflects his growing substance; his London venture provides more conclusive evidence.

Since Sir Robert Mansell had erected glass-houses to be worked by those of Joshua's kinsmen who had gone (with Tyzacks and Titterys) to Newcastle upon Tyne, he had been sending their

[1] Sidesman—then, synodsman; his duty as such was to present twice a year at the visitation of the Ordinary whatever was amiss or irregular in his parish. This duty was later transferred to the Church warden.

window-glass to London by the coasting colliers which supplied the capital with its sea-coal. The crates in which the sheets were packed with straw were sunk to most of their depth in the coal filling the holds of these storm-tossed little ships.[1] Winter weather often delayed the ships' sailing; rough weather in any season caused much loss by breaking. 'To prevent any scarsety of Glasse that might happen in the winter time' in London, Mansell built a glass-house in Woolwich. It proved so unprofitable a venture to him (he knew little about glass-making despite his position in the industry and had to entrust his houses to managers) that in 1639 he was telling the House of Lords 'I ever solde the Glasse made there to my great losse and hindrance'. It is very likely that this was the house taken over by Joshua and managed by his son John; evidence in a later lawsuit suggests that after a time the works was held jointly by the three brothers, Ananias, John and Joshua the Second, though Ananias was busy on ventures of his own in Ireland most of the time and Joshua's interest was wholly in selling the glass at 18s. a case and not in making it.

Like Mansell, they had their difficulties, the glass-house being once shut for a whole year through the breaking of a contract to make 600 cases a year; Joshua claimed damages of over £600 from the delinquent customer; yet they must have made good overall profits.[2] Before John died in 1657, three years before his father, he was in possession of freehold lands in England and Ireland besides the copyhold estate which he had bought for £400 in Kingswinford; this was the Blakemore tenement (afterwards called 'Hawbush') one of the 'customary tenements' of the manor, the tenure of which carried with it the duty of serving in his turn the manorial offices of Biddle, Reeve and Forester; more evidence of the extent to which by now the Lorrainers had become rooted in England. Indeed, John Henzey of Woolwich died an English gentleman.

[1] The colliers on their return journey carried London Ale at first in casks then later in bottles. The colliers usually carried fifty cases of glass per voyage.

As late as 1837 the sister of the Governor-General of India writing about the Nawab of Morshadabad's new palace: 'They have brought out mirrors and large panes of glass for it from England and eight hundred panes were broken in the course of the voyage.'

[2] John's working partners in the Woolwich glasshouse were probably the two Englishmen Robert Taynton and John Oliver who witnessed his will in 1657. John's son, John, who died on the high seas on a voyage to Madagascar, gave directions to this Taynton in his will in 1673; Taynton and Oliver went to work at Newcastle upon Tyne after John's death. A Taynton was in possession of the house in 1701 when the *London Gazette* advertised it 'to be let', 'Enquire of Mr. Taynton at Woolwich'.

Before he died in his sixtieth year, in 1660, Joshua the First had handed over the Brettell glass-house to his sons Paul and Joshua, which meant that, since Joshua spent most of his time in London managing the Woolwich house and marketing by arrangement all the broad-glass made in this district (the whole production of Colemans, the Hooe and Brettell), Paul was in charge of the furnace. By his will Joshua left practically everything to 'Joane my loveinge wife' who was to survive him by twelve years and for whom he had leased a dwelling-house in Amblecote; £30 each for Paul and Joshua and £10 to his daughter Mary, who had married an Englishman named Bradley, were not to be paid until after Joan's death. To his son John's widow and children, whom John had left comfortably off, he left 40s. He had paid off a mortgage of £100 which Ananias had raised on some land he had bought in Brettell; this he forgave as he did also the £26 owed him by his daughter Elizabeth and her husband, Dr. Robert Lloyd.

Ananias, the eldest son, though he had in 1649 bought land next to his father's in Brettell with the probable intention of building his own glass-house there (he did this eventually), for some reason went over to Ireland. He took with him at last the £100 he had raised on his land, complete mastery of the family craft and nearly twenty years' experience as a master of it. Other Lorrainers were already settled there: 'Davy the Frenchman' had been working for the Earl of Cork thirty years before; Abraham Bigoe, father of Abraham who was working with the Tyzacks at Colemans, had done well there and his son Philip better; he had acquired extensive landed estates in King's County.

Ireland had its attractions for English glass-makers long before its later freedom from duties (while these were killing the English industry) drew them in good numbers across the Irish Sea. Ananias Henzey has some historical importance as the first Stourbridge glass-maker to work there. Later, other workmen from this district were to found the industry which produced the famous Irish glass of Waterford and Cork; early Irish glass was Stourbridge glass made in Ireland. According to George Longe, who stated in a petition to Burghley in 1589 that he had spent his whole life in glass-making ('so hath no other englishe man') it would have been a much more practical policy in view of the threat to our national timber supply to reduce the number of glass-houses in England from fifteen to four, to transport the displaced glass-makers to Ireland and build furnaces for them in the woods which abounded there. He had bought the Irish patent and had for two years already proved the suitability of site and available raw materials, and there was this further advantage to English interest, that every glass-house would provide a garrison of twenty men in the very places where they would be most effective in preserving the Queen's rule in Ireland, for the woods in time of rebellion were Elizabeth's worst enemies.[1]

It is hardly likely that Ananias's concern for the Queen's peace (it was not this now, nor the King's but the Commonwealth's) was his reason for emigration. Whatever this was, he found his way to the Bigoes, worked with them and married Philip's daughter, Catherine. While Ananias worked for the day when he, too, could become a landed gentleman, his father-in-law was advancing to rare social heights for a foreigner; (actually he had been naturalized since 1637). In 1662 Philip Bigoe became High Sheriff of King's County; he was still acquiring land and owned a number of glass-houses. Five years later, his son-in-law, now 'Ananias Henzey Esquire', took out a lease of large estates in the same county, including two market towns, a castle and five hamlets. Philip Bigoe died in 1668. Ananias's wife, Catherine, had already been dead some time, but Philip left £300 to his Henzey grandchildren.

Ananias now built a glass-house of his own near Portarlington in Queen's County; there followed a strangely troubled period: his difficulties were so serious that we actually find him unable to pay the rent for his lands; they were technical difficulties: 'I have used all the best ways and means I could to make glass but cannot as yet do it', he writes to his landlord's steward. This comes strangely from a Henzey, a glass-maker with thirty years' experience as a master man. Raw materials were easily available, fuel in plentiful supply: what could Ananias mean? There is only one admissible answer: he was trying to make a different kind of glass, abandoning his family's traditional process, experimenting with new materials. Thorpe suggests that he was attempting to make 'glass of lead', that glass which de Blancourt was a little later to describe as 'beyond doubt the fairest and noblest Glass of any'. In his Savoy glass-house in London at the same time, George

[1] One of the conditions of Abraham Bigoe's original lease in 1623 had been that he should:
    'provide two English or French footmen with muskets or callivers sufficiently provided'
to attend his landlord in His Majesty's service at all times upon two days' warning.

PLATE 8. A famous chair. Tom Cartwright's at Moor Lane, late nineteenth century.

Drawing by Arthur Arrowsmith

PLATE 9.   The Holloway End Cone (demolished 1955)

Ravenscroft was worrying about the same problem; the London Glass Sellers' Company came to his help. Ananias away in the distant solitude of an Irish village, worked without help except the patience of Lord Arlington, his landlord, in waiting for his rent.

Ananias, like all the Lorrainers here, had long used lead in his glass; ever since they had had to cover their pots to protect their metal from the smoke and noxious fumes of the new fuel; this meant that the metal was now receiving no direct heat and lost some of its fusibility and to remedy this loss they added oxide of lead as a flux. Obviously they would make a succession of experiments with gradually increasing amounts of oxide to obtain a workable metal. Maybe Ananias, noticing that the lead was doing more than providing this workable metal—that is, acting as a purely physical agent—was exploiting its possibilities as an ingredient. Whatever materials he was using had to be imported:[1] 'I have sent to Dublin for things to make a further trial', he told the steward, 'and shall not leave off until every expedient has been tried.' The steward put Ananias's case to Lord Arlington, pleaded his long experience, the money he had spent on improving Lord Arlington's land and the new families he had settled on it.[2] What success the steward had with his master, or Ananias with his glass, is not known, but six years later Ananias was still there and thriving sufficiently to be able to set up his son Bigoe Henzey in a glass-house of his own. At much the same time he visited England to build the second Henzey glass-house in Brettell on the land he had bought nearly thirty years before, the house he was to hand over to Bigoe in 1693.

By the Restoration in 1660, the broad-glass industry, despite the Civil War during which this district was systematically plundered by both parties, had become firmly established here. The Lorrainers, by shuffling off their exclusiveness and their close craft secrecy, by marriage and long settlement, were becoming more and more English and already an Englishman (rather a Welshman settled here) had taken over a glass-house: this was

---

[1] Irish glass-makers giving evidence before the Excise Commissioners in 1835 claimed that they had to import their materials, LEAD and Stourbridge Clay being therefore most expensive.

[2] These would be English glass-makers, probably from this district. Sir George Rawdon, in difficulties in an amateur glass-making venture in Ireland in 1665 was writing: 'If any will upon their own account come over and make their own work from Stourbridge . . .' In 1654 and 1655 the Kingswinford Court Rolls mention two tenants as being then in Ireland.

Thomas Rogers, who had married Ann Tittery. Ann's mother had carried on the Hooe glass-house for some time after her husband Daniel's death in 1641; for a time Zachary Tyzack, deserting his uncle at Colemans, had worked it for her. Rogers took over the house and began that long and prosperous connection with the trade which lasted well into the eighteenth century, when another Thomas Rogers left Amblecote and glassmaking for London and banking.

Colemans had been burned down in 1658 and the two Tyzacks, Paul and Zachary, and Abraham Bigoe left it in ruins to go for a time to work at Chelwood in Somerset on contract to Robert Foley; a few months after Joshua Henzey's death they returned, rebuilt it and resumed work there.

At some time in the sixteen-forties a second glass-house had been built in Brettell by Jeremiah Bague, a little to the west of Henzey's on the opposite side of the Dudley–Stourbridge road.[1] Bague had actually come into the district before 1619, for in that year he had married Susanna Henzey at Oldswinford Church. Where and with whom he worked in his first years here we do not know; the vestry appointed him sidesman in 1630; by 1634 he had established himself firmly enough to be 'Mr. Jeremiah Bagg' in the Vestry Book and to be chosen Church Warden with the famous Richard (Fiddler) Foley as his colleague. The next we hear of him is that he is in Greenwich where in partnership with a Francis Bristow he worked a glass-house almost on Sir Robert Mansell's doorstep. In 1641 they fell foul of the monopolist who ordered them to close down. They defied this perfectly legal order and petitioned Parliament for protection while continuing to make their glass. Probably as a result of the 'grievous wrongs and insults' they told Parliament they had suffered at the hands of Mansell, Bague returned to Brettell where his glass-house was certainly at work and he was living in 1650. He was one of the parishioners who in 1653 appointed the Kingswinford parson, Nicholas Paston, to the new office of 'Register' ordained by the Commonwealth parliament.

While the other foreign glass-makers were always referred to as 'broad-glass makers', that is, makers of window-glass by the Lorraine method, Bague was 'glass-maker' pure and simple.

---

[1] Bague's Glass-house site was immediately west of the canal which flows under Brettell Lane. Council houses now stand on it; within living memory the shell of a huge glass-house cone still towered there. The site is marked on the Canal map of 1774.

Production at Colemans, the Hooe and Henzey's Brettell house was practically confined to window-glass; no mention is known of Bague's ever having made this. It is impossible to believe, of course, that such masters of the craft as the men who worked the broad-glass houses did not on occasion make vessels; but there must have been one house, at least, in the district in which vessel-making was the normal activity, for records show that some of the finest vessel-makers of their time lived in this district, which means they worked here. Between 1615 and 1640 the names of many foreign glass-makers, some of them definitely known to have been vessel-makers, appear in the parish registers of the two Swinfords. In 1644, the name of one of the Rachetti family from L'Altare (Mantua), Julius Caesar 'Rackett', appears at Oldswinford. From then on, 'Rackett' appears frequently in the registers of both parishes and the Vestry Book at Oldswinford; they settled in, became Misters, Overseers, Church Wardens. In the sixteen-fifties, three of the Visitalias appear: Abraham, Jacob and Benjamin. Jacob married an Englishwoman, Katherine Hawker, at Bromsgrove in 1656; Abraham 'Wistolia' held the office of Overseer of the poor here in 1655. Later on, in the sixteen-seventies, the Dagnias came: 'Oney Dagney' is the transparent disguise produced by the parish clerk's difficulty with foreign names, which cannot hide the presence of the famous Onesiphorus Dagnia,[1] who about 1685 left the district with his two brothers for Newcastle upon Tyne to introduce lead crystal there and establish a dynasty of glass-makers.

Why did craftsmen of such eminence in vessel-making come to this district? Some writers, including Thorpe, claim that glass-makers here worked in a kind of vacuum sealed off from the rest of the country and out of touch with developments in the industry. The very fact that men like the Rachettis and the Dagnias chose to come to work here is sufficient denial of that claim; they must have heard of the industry's being settled here, and what they heard must have attracted them. Stourbridge glass-makers at this time were very definitely in fairly constant communication with London, Newcastle and Bristol, the three chief glass-making centres. The Henzeys had their Woolwich house, Jeremy Bague his at Greenwich. 'Lorrainers' had a London warehouse on the first floor of Robert Foley's premises in Leadenhall Street; these

---

[1] 'Oney' was fined £200 and costs in 1697 for fraudulently concealing 2679 dozens of glass bottles to evade payment of duty. Two years later Thomas Batchelor of Amblecote had 1000 dozen seized for the same reason.

were obviously the Stourbridge Lorrainers, who often worked on contract with the Foleys, a Stourbridge family; the Newcastle Lorrainers had their warehouse near the Old Swan Stairs. The Foleys had for a time a glass-house at Chelwood (Somerset) within easy reach of Bristol in which city they had premises, it being the natural outlet for the products of the industrially busy Stour and Severn valleys. The Dagnias had a glass-house in Bristol. The Newcastle and Stourbridge Lorrainers were still very closely connected by blood and Sir Robert Mansell had actually transported fireclay from this district to his glass-houses on the Tyne.[1]

Where did these men work? Unfortunately no records remain which give help towards fixing the name or site of any vessel-making house. Indeed, there are no records extant of any other glass-house in the district at this time than Colemans, the Hooe, Henzey's Brettell house and Bague's; the first three definitely specialized in this period in window-glass; only Bague's remains and it is significant that this was the first house to be called a 'White' house.

It was on Paul Henzey, his third son, that Joshua the First's mantle fell in 1660; he now became the busy working leader of the glass industry in the district. He managed the original Brettell House, Ananias's new one, and his mother's estate. He was a good son, cherishing the later years of his mother Joan who lived in Amblecote and his father-in-law, the old Paul Tyzack, who lived with Paul and Ann and their seven children in Ravensitch Coppice in what is now Quarry Bank. Both made him sole executor in their Wills; Paul Tyzack left half of what he had to Paul's children, Joan left Paul all she had

'and all that I have is too little for him'.

Paul's own two sons, Ananias and Paul, did not follow their father's example of filial and family loyalty; Paul by forgery sought to defraud Ananias, Ananias by deceit to rob his father; a tragic experience for one who had been himself so dutiful and true.

[1] Sir George Rawdon knew about Stourbridge glass-makers in Ireland in 1665.

PLATE 10. Ananias Henzey the Third

Sir

Having some unexpected friends Can't wait upon
you to Day but will the first Opportunity one

y^r hum^e Ser^t
Josi^a Hensey
Octo: 2^d 1729

PLATE 11.   Note to North Foley, son of Robert Foley, signed by Joshua Henzey the Third.

Chapter 3

MORE HENZEYS

Wherever the foreign glass-makers went, one complaint was always made against them: Lorrainers, Venetians, Flemings, Normans, all refused to teach their craft to natives whether in England, Paris, Virginia or Ireland. This was, of course, gild practice; their aim was to ensure constant and lasting employment for themselves and their families. In the nineteenth century, members of the Flint Glass Makers' Society were, for a like reason, to protest against the dangerous superfluity of apprentices whom the manufacturers bound or sought to bind to the trade.

The Lorraine industry, a family, father-son affair, faced a similar threat within the family itself: the first Joshua Henzey had four sons, these had ten between them and there were the daughters' sons in addition; there was not room even in an expanding industry for so many gaffers. In 1664, we find the Lorrainers here actually paying one of their number ten shillings a week not to make glass within eighty miles of Stourbridge. Fortunately not all of them wanted to make glass; the second Joshua, for instance, preferred to sell it, to deal with the sheets in a crate in a London warehouse instead of sweating half-naked in front of a Brettell furnace with a hot and heavy cylinder at the end of his blow-pipe. His nephew John, son of that John who managed the Woolwich house, went to sea as 'Master and Comander of the good ship the Coronett'. A third Henzey turned maltster.[1]

Joshua Henzey the second, though like all the young Lorrainers trained in the family craft, decided to become a merchant rather than remain glass-maker like his father. In the same way, Robert Foley took to selling the ironware of which his father, Richard Foley, had originally been a maker. This famous Richard, 'Fiddler Foley', had laid the foundations of the immense fortune that was to be his family's when he introduced the first slitting-mill into the Midlands at Kinver. He had left Dudley, of which

[1] A Paul Tizack (with John Pagett) had left the district for Hagley where the two were making glass in 1678.

23

town he had been mayor, to settle in Stourbridge; there he had come into close touch with the Lorrainers; they worshipped at the same church; his colleague as Church Warden in 1638 was Jeremiah Bague; when he made his will in 1657 he chose Daniel Tittery to witness it.

Among the valuable glass documents in the Palfrey collection is part of a statement of accounts which records the first known business connection between the Foleys and the glassmen. Colemans glass-house had been burned down in 1658; Robert Foley set up the partners who had been working there in Chelwood, Somerset, not far from Bristol where he had trading premises, to make window-glass for him for sale in Bristol or for the coastwise traffic of which that city was the chief port. He paid them 7s. 6d. a case and sold it at 26s. The account deals with 648[1] cases, thirty-six weeks' production at the normal weekly rate for a chair of eighteen cases; probably a full year's work, glass-makers at this time usually working about forty weeks in the year. The statement is receipted by the three partners, Paul Tyzack, his nephew Zacharias and Abraham Bigo and dated September 1660. This was the year in which Robert Foley was appointed official 'Ironmonger to the Navy Office' by James, Duke of York; within a year he had supplied the navy with £5000 worth of ironware.

Foley was an astute business man, as hard-hearted as he was hard-headed, qualities with which traders in this district and in Bristol were well acquainted, and it must have been to Joshua's great satisfaction that Foley proposed that he and Joshua in partnership should buy up the whole production of window-glass here, from the three houses, Colemans, the Hooe and Brettell, and put it on the market. A contract was signed in 1663 for one year; the three houses guaranteed an output of 2400 cases a year and the price agreed was 'at the rate of 20s. by the case'. If no other, rival, glass-house for making window-glass were set up within 'the Space of Eightie miles from a place called Whitimore' (Withymore) then the contract was to continue for two further years.

This seemed to be a most satisfactory agreement to all concerned; it ensured full employment for three years to the makers, each receiving £800 for its year's output, while Foley and Joshua

---

[1] The partners had charged for 649; but Foley accountancy was error-proof. The items of the account suggest that the Lorrainers had to transport the glass to Foley's depot at their own charge; Foley was deducting the cost of their horses' keep from their pay.

By courtesy of
Stevens &
Williams Ltd.

PLATE 12.
The original Moor.
Lane Glass-house.

PLATE 13.

Indenture of the
1703 Perrot-Lorrainer
Agreement.

From the
Palfrey
Collection.

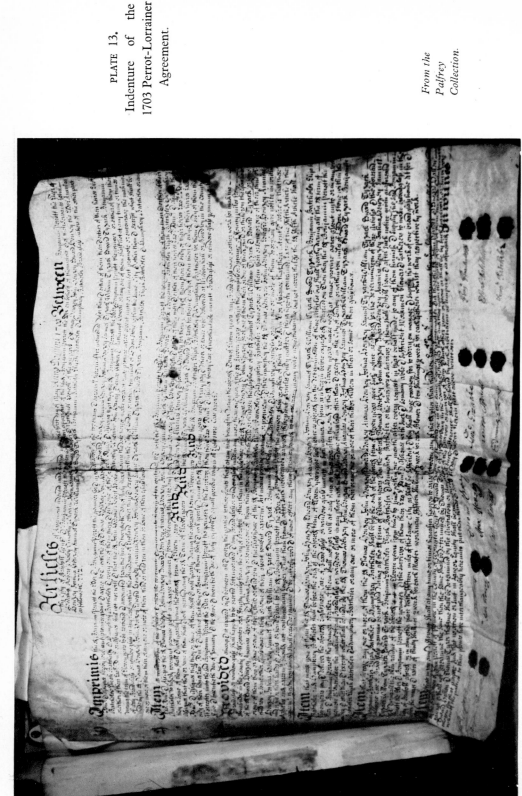

were to reap a clear £720 a year profit without any deduction for expenses, since Joshua's agent was to conduct the sale from this district. Everyone concerned, however, was not satisfied. John Tyzack, elder brother of Paul and working for him at Colemans, thought that he should have a larger share of so lucrative a bargain than a guaranteed wage of 30s. a week for three years gave him; he determined to get it by blackmail, threatening to build a glass-house of his own and so end the contract unless he were paid an extra 10s. a week by the parties making the agreement. Despite John's being, according to contemporary evidence, 'aged weake and troubled with many infirmities' (actually he was only fifty years old) his threat was a potent one which could not be ignored. He was a Tyzack, equally master of the craft as any Henzey or Bigo. He was promised the ten shillings by Joshua; all the contracting parties were to pay their shares, Joshua Henzey, Paul Henzey and Paul Tyzack 2s. 6d. each, the contractor Foley 1s. 6d. while Abraham Bigo and Zacharias Tyzack paid 6d. each. This was to be paid by one Oseland, Joshua's 'agent, bayliffe, clarke or overseer' who was in complete charge of all window-glass made and its sale.

In June 1665 for some reason John Tyzack was discharged from Colemans and Oseland no longer paid him the ten shillings. John immediately brought an action in the Court of Exchequer against Joshua and Oseland. Tyzack did not give the alleged reason for his dismissal but Oseland stated that within the first year a new glass-house was set up by —— Hickman[1] within seventy miles; that, despite this, the contract had been allowed to stand and Tyzack for a time still received his ten shillings. He was probably suspected of some responsibility for the new house and for this was sacked.

It was a strange case; at first Tyzack claimed that Joshua had made a written promise of the ten shillings and that for some time Oseland as his clerk had paid it; half-way through the case he dropped the charge against Joshua and claimed that it was Oseland who had guaranteed the payment on his own account and Joshua actually supported him in this. Suddenly Joshua left the country for Ireland where he arrived to find his elder brother

---

[1] The document recording this evidence is torn; the Hickman family was a substantial Stourbridge one. Oseland's 'within seventy miles' was probably a mistake for the 'eighty' in the contract. The christian name of the Hickman which is missing would have helped to identify him more closely.

In 1699 a Richard Hickman of Stourbridge was a sleeping partner in the second Henzey glass-house in Brettell.

Ananias just taking possession of the 'Two market towns with fair and markets belonging, a castle and five hamlets'; he followed suit and obtained a grant of lands in the same Kings County.

Within six months he was dead and the case was continued by his widow Dorothy in conjunction with Tyzack. Joshua had left no will and Dorothy obtained letters of administration of his estate. Oseland claimed that Joshua had died 'possessed of a very great personall estate, sufficient to pay all his debts and funeralls' and the £40 claimed by Tyzack, 'with a very great overplus worth five Hundred Pounds and upwards'. Dorothy pleaded poverty.

The result of the case is not known; all the evidence agreed first that Joshua definitely promised the ten shillings and that Oseland was merely his agent and had no part in the agreement nor share in the business.

Joshua's change of attitude during the case is difficult to explain; as we shall see there was a streak of untrustworthiness in the Henzeys which was to show very prominently in the next generation. Financial trouble, failure of the Woolwich house which was his special concern, may have decided his flight to Ireland. Did he lease land there to build a glass-house and launch a new venture? This could explain Tyzack's behaviour, too.

Was it because he saw that it was most unlikely that he would get anything from Joshua that he turned on Oseland?

Who and what was Oseland? Can we trust his evidence? Oseland was not merely somebody with a gift for figures and salesmanship which had recommended his employment as agent to Joshua. He was the Rev. Henry Oseland, M.A., of Trinity College, Cambridge, who had been Rector of Bewdley and was Joshua's brother-in-law, having married his widowed sister, Mary Bradley, in 1660. In 1662, refusing to conform to the articles of the Act of Uniformity of that year he had been ejected from his living; he was among the best-known of the 'Bartholomew Divines'. Richard Baxter esteemed him highly as 'the most lively fervent moving preacher in all the county; of an honest upright life'; he lived in an aura of golden public opinion and when he was buried at Kingswinford Church in 1703 no fewer than twelve funeral sermons were preached for him.

It is hardly likely that such a man would lie under oath when he gave his evidence before the four magistrates commissioned to take this at the 'Cock Inn', Stourbridge. The four justices were the well-known Captain Andrew Yarranton[1]—who was later to make the Stour navigable from Stourbridge to Kidderminster— Edward Persehouse, Lord Dudley's steward, Robert Lloyd, Joshua's brother-in-law and doctor, and Richard Smart.

Some matters of trade interest appear in the evidence; the gaffer's standard wage of 30s. a week, the wage which Paul Tyzack was paying his nephew Zacharias in 1645 and which the Stourbridge gaffer was still to get in 1703; the anticipation of a modern business practice of paying a potential competitor to keep out of the market. The Henzey-Foley contract was not an attempt to monopolize the Stourbridge glass industry;[2] neither man was a glass manufacturer. Henzey, though nominally possessing a half-share in the Brettell house in trust for his mother, was a merchant; to Foley, glass must have been the smallest of sidelines; at the time there was money in it, which he could levy as a toll on its passage through the channels he had cut for his immense traffic in ironware; he lived practically all the year in London, a fact of which his wife[3] in Stourbridge was constantly complaining, and probably did nothing more than sign receipts for the £360 a year he was making out of the contract.

Joshua Henzey the Second had lived most of his life in Woolwich. Factual records of him are rare; there are none of his birth or marriage, the Woolwich registers commenced too late to record these,[4] and the only known record of his death is an approximate one from Oseland's evidence in the Tyzack case.

Fortunately we know much more of his eldest son Thomas who was to make a vigorous attempt to revive the dying broad-glass industry here at the beginning of the next century and, while failing in this, succeeded in establishing the Henzeys firmly in a new glass world.

Paul Henzey, who was in charge of the Brettell house and seems never to have left the district, was not so fortunate in his sons, Ananias and Paul Junior, as Joshua was in Thomas. Shortly before his early death, John of Woolwich, brother to Paul and Joshua, had bought the Hawbush estate in Brettell. When he died in 1657

---

[1] Yarranton, a Parliamentary officer during the Civil War, and Oseland had suffered imprisonment together as suspected conspirators in 'Packington's Plot', a proposed rising by Presbyterians and disgruntled Roundhead veterans.

[2] As claimed in the article on Glass in the *Victoria County History of Worcestershire*.

[3] Ann, daughter of Lord North; she lived in the Foleys' 'Brick House' now the 'Talbot Hotel'.

[4] Woolwich Registers began in 1670.

this came into the possession of his son John, then not yet of age but already restive in the confines of continuous cylinder blowing and readier to risk the hazards of the high seas; and he went to sea. What journeys he made before his last fatal sailing are not known but they must have been many and successful, for he left England for the last time as 'Master and Comander of the Coronett'. Probably to finance this venture John sold Hawbush to his uncle Paul, who invested in it to guarantee the future of his younger children.

Paul paid £370 of the £520 purchase price and had the property made over to his eldest son Ananias in trust for himself. John from London sent down his letter of attorney authorizing the transfer to Ananias. The attorney was Joshua Bradley of Wordsley, the biggest landowner in the Kingswinford manor. By some means Paul junior got this letter into his hands, erased the name 'Ananias' and wrote in his own. The surrender to Paul according to the forged terms was actually carried out with all the traditional solemn formalities of the manorial court:

> 'to whom the lord by his steward hath granted seizin of the same and thereof he hath seizin by the rod according to the custom of the manor to have and to hold to the said Paul Henzey his heirs &c. by the rents services and customs therefore due and of right accustomed.'

Paul paid his fine of £15 10s. to the steward, did his fealty and left the Court, owner of Hawbush and a customary tenant of the manor. It was some months before the fraud was proved and matters righted. Paul's attempt to defraud his brother is recorded by this marginal note in the Court Rolls:

> 'The letter of attorney (by which this Surr.[1] past) was altred agt the will of him that signed it and without the privity of the Lord or his steward, Ananias beinge razed out and Paul putt in and therefore voyd. And therefore Mr. John Henzey signd . . .'

The last lines of this note cannot be read as they were sewed through in binding, but enough is there to damn Paul.

This act of deceit was not the only family tragedy to be played on the Hawbush stage. A second act followed fourteen years later with Ananias now as villain.

Paul senior had raised a mortgage of £300 on Hawbush with Sir Walter Wrottesley. Sir Walter died in 1690 and his executor called in the mortgage. Paul borrowed the £300 (from Henry

---

[1] 'Surrender.'

PLATE 14.
The Coal-
bournbrook
Glass-houses
in 1844.
The house,
John Henzey's
'Harlestones'
is now the
offices of
Webb Corbett
Ltd.

*From the
Palfrey
Collection.*

PLATE 15. Designer and Gaffer, from Certificate of Membership of
Glassmakers' Friendly Society 1850. This Symbolic group,
suggested by Benjamin Richardson, was used also by the
Glasscutters' Society for its certificate.

Pretty of Oldswinford) and handed the money to Ananias to repay it and redeem the lands 'not doubting the least of his integrity and asked him to bring back the deeds'; Ananias refused to return them. When Paul was forced by his continued obstinacy to sue him for them Ananias made two contradictory excuses for withholding them; first that he had not yet paid over the money and so had not received the deeds, and second that the money with which he had repaid the mortgage was his own. Again the result of Paul's case is unknown, but there is evidence that Ananias actually pressed Henry Pretty to sue his father for the £300 he had borrowed. Hawbush passed altogether from the Henzeys in 1702.

Benjamin, youngest of the three sons of Joshua the Second and cousin to the Hawbush delinquents, challenged cousin Paul's right to be the only forger in the family. When the Woolwich house was in difficulties and Joshua, his father, had gone (maybe to escape his creditors) to Ireland, Benjamin was out of work. His cousin, Captain John of the *Coronet*, preparing for a trading voyage to Madagascar and hearing of Ben's low condition, offered him the post of steward aboard his ship and Ben accepted. Captain John died on the high seas during the voyage which in every other matter was a particularly prosperous one. John's share of the profits, according to the ship's officers, should have been about £1000. The cargo had been chiefly of lengths of cloth which had been sold in African ports; negroes had been bought and transported across the Atlantic to serve as slaves in the Barbadoes; the cargo on the homeward journey had been 'sugars and other comodities'. It was the type of round voyage which was to make many a British fortune in the years to come.

As soon as John Henzey was dead, Benjamin, claiming to be his next-of-kin and despite the protests of the ship's officers who tried to insist on an inventory of his goods being taken, took possession of everything. He transferred £100 in pieces of eight and quantities of sugar, ivory, muslins, silks and wine to other ships, which were homeward bound before the *Coronet* set out for Barbadoes, for his own use when he returned to England.

The voyage over and the *Coronet* and its rich cargo safe in London, Benjamin produced a book which he said was Captain John's account book, on one page of which were three entries of which the first read:

'Received of my Cosen Beniamine Henzy upon an Adventure fifty pounds sterling'.

Presenting this to John's mother, Benjamin asked for the £50 and his proportionate share of the profits of the voyage. She denied that the entries were in her son's handwriting and pointed out that they were neither signed nor witnessed, 'grosse mistakes' of which such an 'exact punctuall man and good accomptant' as her son John could not have been guilty. The second entry recorded the receipt of £24 on the same basis from John's sister Elizabeth. Elizabeth denied having invested any money in her brother's venture. The third entry was also false in fact.

John's mother not only refused Benjamin's demand but also counter-claimed from him what he had appropriated of John's belongings.

Whatever his aunt Mary thought of him, Benjamin's mother thought better for she made him sole executor of her will by which she left him, after twenty shillings to her eldest son Thomas and one shilling to her second son Edward, £200 and all her goods and chattels.

Paul Henzey in his later years must often have pondered anxiously on the future of the broad-glass industry in the hands of such men as he too well knew his sons to be; the standing of the family was in danger, too. Who was the Henzey who could worthily follow himself as head of the family and leading glass-maker in the district?

His eldest brother Ananias's son, Bigoe, was lord of lands in Ireland and, like his father's, his connection with the district was almost wholly nominal. (Paul was managing the glass-house Ananias had built in Brettell.) Of brother John's sons, Captain John had been buried at sea and Elisha had died a bachelor in London. What of Joshua's three? Benjamin had blotted his escutcheon but he was the youngest and could be left to make what he could with what his doting mother had left him. But the other two, Thomas and Edward, were more promising candidates.

Thomas must have restored the derelict Woolwich business his father had outrun to a new prosperity. His bride's dowry may have helped him to do this for he had married into a wealthy family. In the same year, 1667, as his father attempted to start afresh in Ireland, Thomas married Frances Croker, co-heiress of a Gloucestershire landowner. Edward came home (for that is what this district now meant to the Henzeys) also to marry into a family of substance, the Jestons, who were shortly to begin glass-making themselves. His bride was Rose, daughter of Edward Jeston, cloth manufacturer of Stourbridge. On the same day John Jeston

PLATE 16.   The Holloway End Glass-house, 1820.

PLATE 17.   Saturday morning—filling the pot.

married Mary, daughter of Paul Henzey, so John joined the
Henzeys in trade as well as wedlock for he became a glass-maker.

On his marriage, Edward settled here and worked for his uncle
Paul in the glass-house he was managing for Ananias. Thomas
was still living at Woolwich but found time to travel to Ireland
and to invest capital in Kings County. But in 1676 he too came
home to spend the rest of his life in an attempt to save the Stourbridge broad-glass industry which was just beginning to feel the
growing strength of that public demand for crown-glass which
was to drive the Lorrainers' broad-glass out of the market.

His uncle Paul watched with proud approval Thomas's gradual
assumption of his leadership of the industry, knowing it to be now
in responsible hands. His son, Ananias, was still to trouble his last
years but he was not to suffer the lonely anxiety he had feared.
His particular personal affairs he now entrusted to John Parnell
of Amblecote, a son-in-law.

Paul died in 1693 and so fortunately was spared the experience
of those years of Glass Duties which almost killed the English
glass industry just as this seemed to have become capable of
standing on its own firm feet without any of that support from
foreign glass-makers which had so long been indispensable. Two
years before his death he had shown his affection for the church
he had attended so faithfully so long by the gift of a

> 'large silver Bole with his coate of Armes engraved thereon
> to bee and remaine for the use and behoofe of the parishioners
> of Oldswinford att the Sacrament for ever.'

His delinquent sons, Paul and Ananias, were not forgotten in
their father's will:

> 'to my two sonns Ananias and Paul five shillings apiece'.

He entrusted all his affairs to his executor John Parnell, praying
him to take especial care that neither his sons nor his sons-in-law
should have any power

> 'to sett sell assyne or otherwise dispose of it or part of'

his estate; that must remain in the family.[1]

---

[1] In the next year a Tyzack was to tie up his estate in the same way so that
'it should continue in the name and blood of us the said Tyzacks'.

Chapter 4

FLINT GLASS AND THE COMING OF CROWN

In 1696, John Houghton, Fellow of the Royal Society, in the 198th of those Letters he published 'for the Improvement of Commerce and Trade', gave a list of the eighty-eight[1] glass-houses then existing in England and Wales, with some details of the kind of glass they made. This, the first published list, shows very plainly the important part the Stourbridge industry was taking in national production; of the eighty-eight, twenty-four stood in the London district, eleven in 'Newcastle-upon-Tine' and no less than seventeen in 'Stowerbridge'. Of these seventeen, only seven were still producing that broad-glass which had so long been the staple product here; five were bottle-houses, the other five were making 'flint green ordinary'.[2]

Examination of inventories of the time discloses that very few people—even the glass-makers themselves—possessed glass of any kind save that in their windows which, since it was no longer the removable chattel it had been until 1599, was not included in such lists. In 1695, in the many rooms of the 'Talbot Inn' there were, for instance, only two mirrors (and these, a 'Chimney piece glass' and 'one great glass' both in the 'Blew Room') and 'two glass potts' in the pantry-kitchen.[3] Elizabeth Bague in 1674 had 'one Beare (beer) Goblett'; John Henzey of Harlestones, Amble-cote, in 1717 had '50 case of broad-glass'. However, the Talbot's pantry-kitchen harboured 'seventeen dozen bottles'; John Henzey had twenty dozen, pints and quarts, while in 1685, Paul Tyzack of Hagley had a 'Stock in Bottles, £30'. Lord Ward of Dudley

---

[1] Houghton heads his list: 'An Account of all the Glasshouses in England and Wales'. He seems to have missed one unless this had been built after 1696.
In 1697 Celia Fiennes reported: 'Castleton Bridge (Derbyshire) where there was a glasshouse: we saw them, blowing white glass and neale it in a large oven by the heate of ye furnace.'

[2] See page 50.

[3] It is a pity that nothing is known of these 'two glass potts'; they may have been posset-pots, which were usually highly decorated vessels of master crafts-manship. Elizabeth Bague's goblet may have been made here; numerous bases from beakers, beer-glasses, have been found on Lorrainer sites in England.

Castle leasing 'mines of clay fitt for the makeing of Glasshouse potts in Ravensitch Coppice' fixed the rent in 1709 at

'£100 per annum and one hundred and Twenty Quarts of good sound marketable merchantable and well-condicioned wine with glass bottles to contain the same on 25 December to be delivered yearly at the Talbott Inn in Stowerbridge'.

The making of bottles as opposed to the viols (phials) for apothecaries which were always being made in little cribs, was a branch of the trade established by Sir Robert Mansell. But what of flint glass?

'Stourbridge Flint Glass' was later to gain world renown, yet it is doubtful if any 'flints' were ever used by any Stourbridge glass-maker; not even the broad-glass makers mention them in their stocks; ashes, kelp, coal, clay, crates but never flints, although the early Lorrainers had used them in England; calcined flints have been found on their sites.

The glass-maker throughout history had always in his mind rock crystal as the ideal for which he must strive; crystalline glass was the goal. In 1662 another Fellow of the Royal Society, Christopher Merret, had translated the Italian Antonio Neri's *L'Arte vetraria* into English and so provided the glass-makers of this country with their first primer. Neri tells how the Venetians at Murano instead of sand used a hard white marble and pebbles from the bed of the river Ticino which they burned, then ground 'into a most impalpable powder' from which they were able to make an 'incomparable pure and white Crystall Metall'.

But for successful experiments with another ingredient which produced the 'whitest' metal ever yet made in England there is little doubt that some glass-makers would have persisted, despite the great cost and labour of pulverising them, in using flints; 'nothing but the Parcimony and Covetousness of the times has brought sand in use again' wrote a contemporary; to-day he would have attributed it to 'the profit-motive'.

The ingredient which had achieved this was lead; the new glass was 'Glass of Lead, beyond doubt the fairest and noblest Glass; if this Glass were as tough as Crystal it would surpass it in beauty . . . a perticuler sort of Christaline Glasse resembling Rock Christall not formerly exercised or used in this Kingdome.' But glass of lead was not something new; the Lorrainers here had used oxide of lead as a flux in attempts to obtain a more readily fusible mixture when they were forced to cover their pots on the first use of coal as fuel. It cannot be believed that such glass-makers would not notice the effect of this on the colour of their metal nor that they did not use more and more of it; window-glass makers would exploit any material which produced more translucent glass. The technical difficulties which caused Ananias Henzey such trouble in Ireland in the sixteen-fifties were probably encountered in attempts to make a successful lead glass. Official recognition of success with the new glass is given to George Ravenscroft, a London shipowner who was an 'ingenious gentleman' with a lively interest in chemistry. His experiments were first carried out in his own glass-house but soon the London Glass Sellers' Company gave him financial backing and Ravenscroft produced that lead crystal glass with the 'distinction of sound discernible by any person whatsoever'.

At first Ravenscroft had used flints, but the glass which he handed over to English glass-makers when he made no attempt to renew his patent in 1681, was glass of lead. Yet the name by which this glass became famous was 'flint glass'. In 1696 Houghton wrote:

> 'Our glassmen for making the best flint glass use instead of powdered flints a very fine white sand such as we strow upon writing.'

While H. J. Powell, a practical glass-maker, claims that this lead glass was not the result of a 'sudden invention of Ravenscroft' but of successive tentative experiments to make a more readily fusible glass, W. A. Thorpe, historian of English glass-making, asserts very confidently that it was an invention 'in the stricter sense of the word, the result of an attempt conceived deliberately and carried out experimentally to provide a sound commercial substitute for rock crystal'.

Whether Ravenscroft wears his laurels of right or not, Stourbridge glass-makers were making this glass long before the seventeenth century was out. Thomas Rogers of Amblecote, at the old Hooe house, is spoken of as making 'white' glass; Bague's in Brettell and Dennis as 'white' houses. Houghton's letter in 1696 gives the number of white houses here as five, while Edward Houghton, a local glass-maker, in evidence given to the House of Commons in 1698 mentions '6 or 7'.

Hardly had the new flint glass become established here when the whole structure of the industry was severely shaken in 1695 by the imposition by the Government of Excise duties. The war against France, the new King William's answer to Louis XIV's attempt to restore the Stuarts to the English throne, had begun

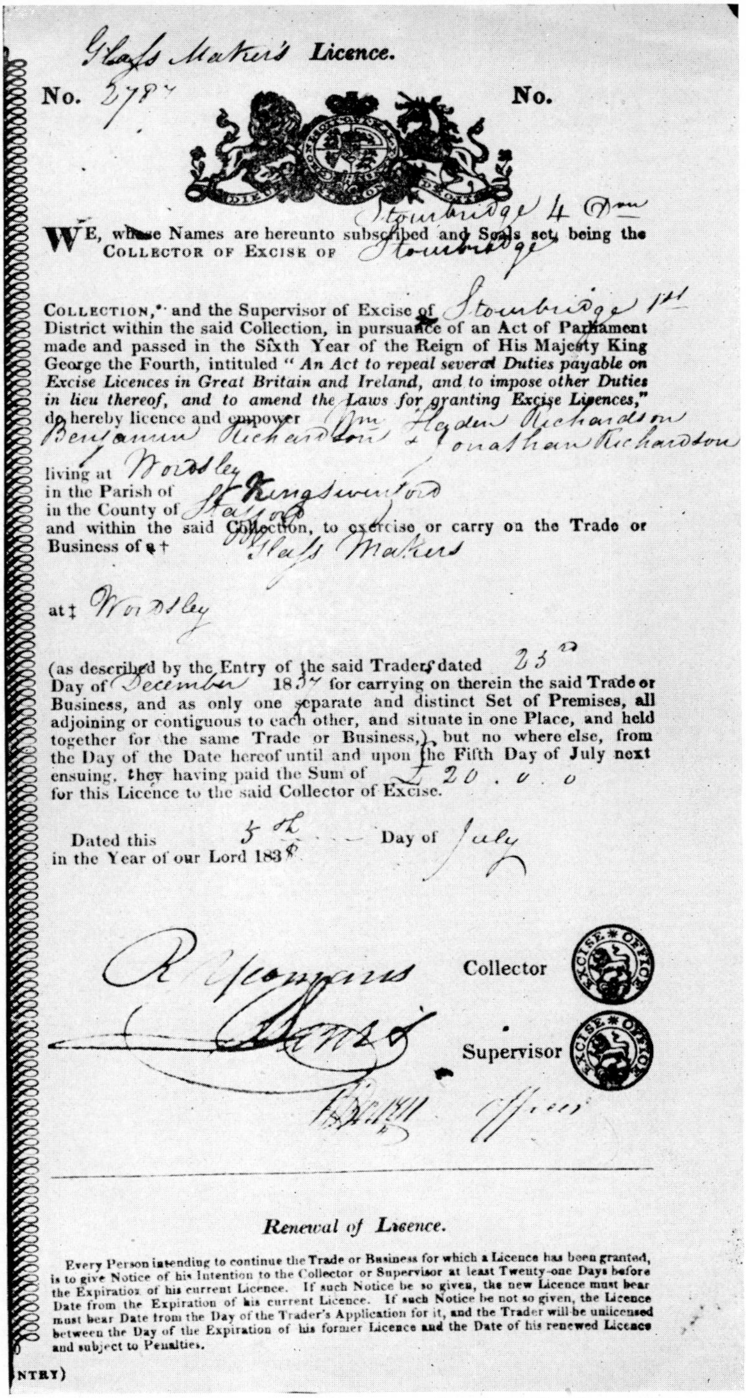

Glass Maker's Licence.

No. 3787   No.

WE, whose Names are hereunto subscribed and Seals set, being the COLLECTOR OF EXCISE OF *Stourbridge* 4 *Dow*
Stourbridge

COLLECTION, and the Supervisor of Excise of *Stourbridge 1st*
District within the said Collection, in pursuance of an Act of Parliament made and passed in the Sixth Year of the Reign of His Majesty King George the Fourth, intituled " *An Act to repeal several Duties payable on Excise Licences in Great Britain and Ireland, and to impose other Duties in lieu thereof, and to amend the Laws for granting Excise Licences,*" do hereby licence and empower *Wm Hayden Richardson Benjamin Richardson & Jonathan Richardson*

living at *Wordsley*
in the Parish of *St Kingswinford*
in the County of *Stafford*
and within the said Collection, to exercise or carry on the Trade or Business of *Glass Makers*

at *Wordsley*

(as described by the Entry of the said Traders dated *25*
Day of *December* 1837 for carrying on therein the said Trade or Business, and as only one separate and distinct Set of Premises, all adjoining or contiguous to each other, and situate in one Place, and held together for the same Trade or Business,) but no where else, from the Day of the Date hereof until and upon the Fifth Day of July next ensuing, they having paid the Sum of *£ 20 . 0 . 0* for this Licence to the said Collector of Excise.

Dated this *5th* Day of *July*
in the Year of our Lord 1838

Collector

Supervisor

Renewal of Licence.

Every Person intending to continue the Trade or Business for which a Licence has been granted, is to give Notice of his Intention to the Collector or Supervisor at least Twenty-one Days before the Expiration of his current Licence. If such Notice be so given, the new Licence must bear Date from the Expiration of his current Licence. If such Notice be not so given, the Licence must bear Date from the Day of the Trader's Application for it, and the Trader will be unlicensed between the Day of the Expiration of his former Licence and the Date of his renewed Licence and subject to Penalties.

(NTRY)

By courtesy of the Librarian, Brierley Hill Library Collection.

PLATE 18.   Glass-maker's Licence issued to
the Richardson brothers, 1837.

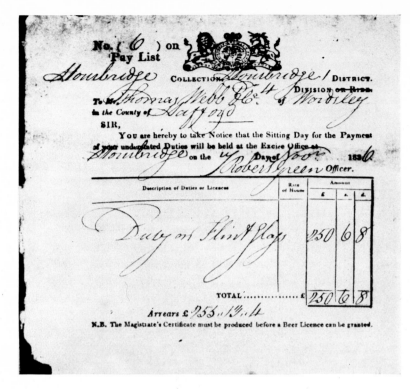

(a)

PLATE 19. (a) Demand Note for Excise Duties, 1836.
(b) Receipt for payment of Excise Duties, 1829.

(b)

in 1689; by 1695 the costs of the war forced the Exchequer into this scheme for taxing certain industries. 'Tis very strange', wrote one pamphleteer, 'that all our other Manufactures should be under a Noli me tangere and this of Glass and Earthen Ware should be singled out to be crushed to Ruine.' What was at first proclaimed an emergency measure but was made permanent in the following year, imposed a 20 per cent duty on flint glass and one of a shilling a dozen on bottles. For some reason the Government gave the industry four months' notice of its intention with the result that the manufacturers piled up great stocks of what would be duty-free glass; the Excise Commissioners said that they stocked themselves and their retailers with, in some cases, a year's supply. While most of the London glass-houses continued production throughout the taxed years and actually paid two-thirds of the whole amount that was raised from the duties, it was claimed that fifty-five out of sixty-one provincial houses closed down and the rest went on short time; in this district it was claimed in 1698 that four bottle-houses had not worked 'since the duty' while the others had kept open for only seven or eight weeks of the usual forty in the year.

The imposition of these duties was not so novel[1] or surprising as the reaction of the industry to them. For four years by every means, by petition to and attendance at the House of Commons, by tract and pamphlet, by meetings and demonstrations, English glass-makers fought their Government, and none more determinedly than those of the Stourbridge district, on a battlefield that covered the whole country and won a victory which must have been one of the most remarkable in industrial history. In 1699, after the House had appointed a Committee of Inquiry which found that the duties were grievous to manufacturers while bringing 'little Advantage to the King' and that, if they were continued there was a danger of the glass industry 'being lost to the Kingdom', the duties were withdrawn.

Much may be learned of conditions and practices in the industry of that time from the petitions presented to Parliament during this anti-duty campaign, if they are checked by the comments of

---

[1] On 24 November 1645 an Ordinance for Additional Excise had decreed a duty of:

'12d every 20 shilling value of Glass of all sorts made in the Kingdom to be paid by the Maker.'

On 26 June 1657 again:

'For all sorts of glass upon every twenty shillings value to be paid by the Maker one shilling.'

D   35

the Commissioners on 'the Fictions and Falsities' to which the glass-makers had been 'forced to fly'. Edward Houghton, for instance, claimed in evidence given to the House of Commons that there were 950 persons employed in glass-houses in the Stour-bridge district; the Commissioners denied this, 'there being not 800 people employed in or about all the Glasse Works in England'. John Bague and John Jeston, who worked in Brettell, putting the case for themselves, 'and other glassmakers in and about Stourbridge' said that the 'many hundred Families they employed in making Glass Bottles' had not worked since the Duty commenced; the Commissioners agreed that there may have been less demand for bottles at Stourbridge, but pointed out that the bottle trade here depended on the cider trade in the Severn valley and no cider having been made there for two years the demand for bottles had naturally fallen off. Ananias Henzey and Elisha Batchelor complained that the duty had increased the price of bottles and the public would buy only cheap ones; they claimed, too, that the use of bottles depended 'more upon Fancy than Necessity'. The Commissioners retorted that bottles were actually cheaper since the duties had been imposed not because of the duties but because the glass-makers here had lowered their prices 'to destroy others who were setting up against them'. If bottles only tickled the users' fancy 'then no poor man need part with his Money'. When the glass-makers grumbled about the huge stocks of bottles which they could not sell, forty thousand dozen of them, the Commissioners asked why there were none on sale anywhere. When the local glassmen named the houses which the duties had closed, the Commissioners claimed that the flint and broad-glass makers here had not closed down 'until they were desired to stop by Letters from London to make a Pretence for Petitioning'.

Despite the special pleading of the Commissioners who naturally very carefully chose the items on which to comment, Parliament passed a 'Repeal Act' which decreed that the duties 'shall cease determine and be no longer payable paid or collected on and after August 1'. Less than half a century later a further attempt (and this time a successful one) was made to fasten fiscal burdens on the industry, burdens which all the efforts of the trade throughout a century failed to throw off.

A short time before the Repeal Act was passed, in the early months of the same year, one of the new English glass-makers in this district, Thomas Batchelor, who had cut Paul Henzey's sheets into pane sizes at Brettell but had left to make bottles on his own account at Dennis in 1691, fell foul of the exciseman. Batchelor had been selling his bottles without supplying the official with that statement on which duty was reckoned; his rather foolish attempt to evade payment resulted in his stock of a thousand dozen bottles being seized. In petitioning the Glass Commissioners for the return of this stock he pleaded ignorance. In view of the voluminous outcry of protest which had gone on for more than three years in this district against the duties, and the fact that his brother Elisha had actually given evidence to the House of Commons on their dire effect on the industry here, this plea was patently false. He added poverty to ignorance as an extenuating circumstance. The Treasury's response to his request was hardly as lenient as it sounds; its warrant to the Commissioners ordered indeed the return of his stock but on condition that he paid the duty (£50), the expenses of the seizers and a gratuity to them; their mercy was granted 'he being poor and ignorant and this being his first offence'. Since excise officers were paid partly on a share basis of what they seized, the officer here, knowing Batchelor, would certainly be less inclined to consider him poor and ignorant than Treasury officials in Whitehall and his gratuity would be graded according to this superior knowledge. On 13 December 1749 Ben Ord, the local exciseman, was giving a second Thomas Batchelor, wiser than his father, a receipt for £249 12s. 2d. 'for the Duty on Glass chargd according to the Acts of Parliament in that behalf made'; in the space headed 'Arrears' Ben Ord had not found it necessary to enter anything.[1]

Pride in the achievement of the English industry in producing the new glass shines out of the pleas and protests of the petitions: masters and workmen had brought 'the Glass manufacture to so great Perfection'; 'the Makers of Flint Glasses had beaten out all Foreigners meerly by making these Commodities better'; 'We Are the Artists of the World.'

Let us look at these artists. According to one tract published during the anti-Duty campaign, 'the wages of Glassmakers is already so small (that considering the Heat & Slavery of their Work which causes greater Expense to Support Nature than Cooler Trades do) tis as much as they can do to keep Life and Soul together.' No figures are given but we know from other sources that the gaffer, blower and gatherer were receiving respective weekly wages of 30s., 15s. and 10s. for the forty weeks of the year which glass-makers then normally worked, that is £60, £30 and

[1] This receipt is in the Palfrey Collection.

£20 a year; in the money values of those days, these were exceedingly good wages such as only a prosperous industry could have afforded to pay. The postmistress at Stourbridge was paid at the same time £10 a year. The workmen were engaged by contract for three, four, five or sometimes as long as seven years, under the conditions of which the manufacturer was 'obliged to Imploy or pay them Play-Wages for nothing'. They worked then the same six-hour shift, six hours on, six hours off, as they were to work until the years immediately before the Second World War.[1] The square furnace the Lorrainers had always used was now being superseded by the round, such as the glass-makers of Germany and the Low Countries used. The Stourbridge round furnace, however, was not a copy of this, but a type invented by an Oldswinford man, William Tristram, who came of a family of Rectors. Had Tristram lived in or near London he would probably have been another member of the Royal Society interested in glassmaking, for he was a most 'ingenious gentleman' who not only 'greatly improved the art of making fflint-glass but of purifying iron for making steel'.[2]

The buildings housing the new round furnaces grew higher and higher and the huge cones[3] that for long so strikingly labelled this district as a glass-making centre appeared. The *London Gazette* of 22 June 1702 reports one '94 Foot high and 60 Foot broad'. At first the erection of these cones presented difficulties the builders did not always successfully overcome. Captain Philip Roche began building one in Dublin in 1696; twice it collapsed, killing seven men on one occasion; his third effort succeeded and the cone weathered a century's storms. In 1700, 'a new Glasshouse that cost near £2000 and was never used fell down on Saturday last of itself'.

Nearly a hundred years later, on 6 October 1785, George Ensell's glass-house at Coalbournbrook, Amblecote, 'fell almost entirely in ruins to the ground'. Between these years, newspapers

---

[1] The first firm to abandon this shift was Stevens & Williams in 1936.

[2] Tristram's brother was the Andrew Tristram, Rector of Rowley and Clent, who was ejected from that living under the terms of the Act of Uniformity, 1662.

[3] Rarely truly conical but ellipsoidal in shape. What was probably the oldest cone still standing in the country, that of the Holloway End glasshouse, Amblecote, was demolished in 1955. A Belfast News-Letter of August 19, 1785, reported a new glass-house, 120 feet high 'being the largest in Great Britain or Ireland'. In 1823 one was to let in Belfast the cone of which was 150 feet high. An Act of the Irish Parliament in 1783 decreed that no glass-house chimney should be less than 50 feet high.

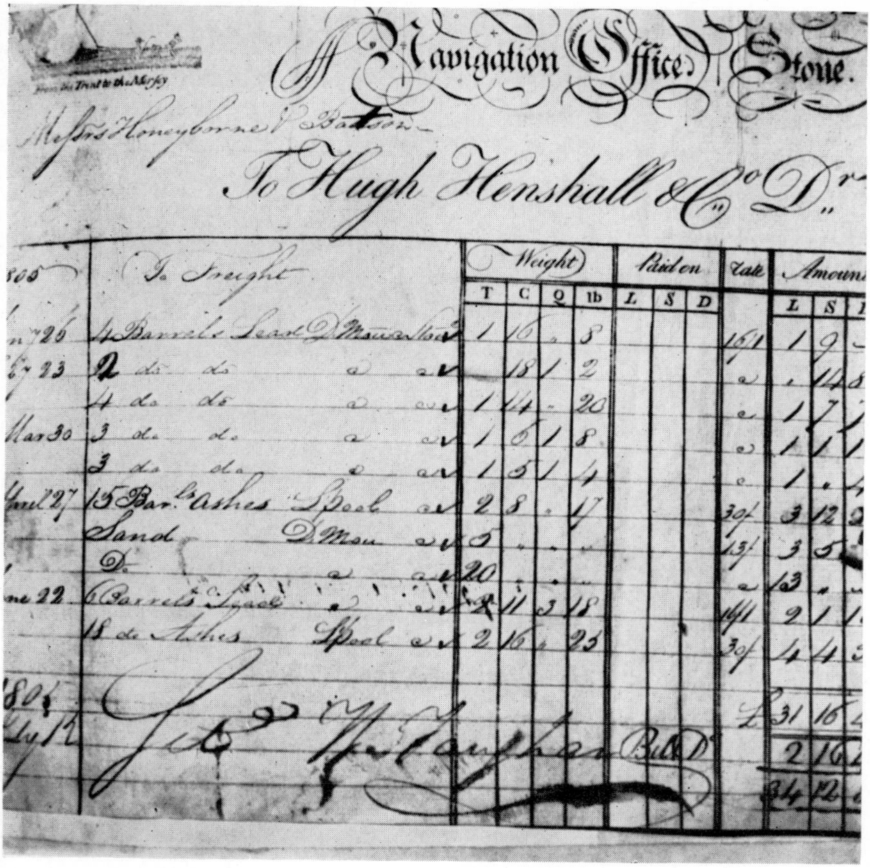

From the Trent to the Mersey

Navigation Office Stone.

Messrs Honeyborne & Batson

To Hugh Henshall & Co Dr

1805	To Freight	Weight T	C	Q	lb	Paid on L	S	D	Rate	Amount L	S	D
Jan 26	4 Barrels Lead D. Manc	1	16	.	8				16/1	1	9	
Feb 23	2 do do do		18	1	2				do	.	14	8
	4 do do do	1	14	-	20				do	1	7	
Mar 30	3 do do do	1	6	1	8				do	1	1	
	3 do do do	1	5	1	4				do	1	.	
April 27	15 Barls Ashes Lpool	2	8	.	17				30/	3	12	
	Sand D Mon	5							13/	3	5	
	Do do	20							do	13	.	
June 22	6 Barrels Lead do	2	11	3	18				16/1	2	1	
	18 do Ashes Lpool	2	16	.	23				30/	4	4	
									£	31	16	
										2	16	
1805 July 12	Bill Dr									34	12	

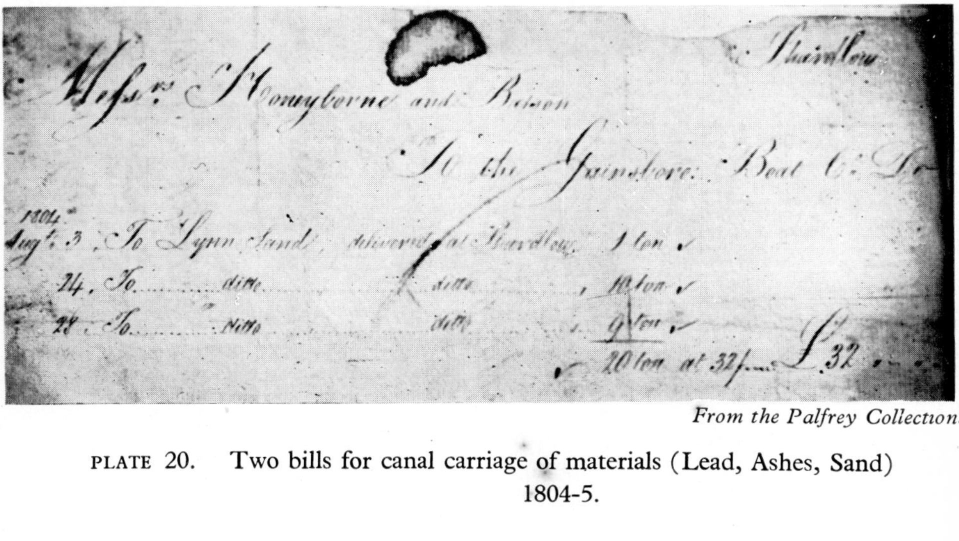

Messrs Honeyborne and Batson

Shardlow

To the Gainsboro' Boat Co. Dr

1804 Augt 3 To Lynn Sand, delivered at Shardlow 1 ton

24 To ditto ditto 10 ton

28 To ditto ditto 9 ton

20 ton at 32/ £32

From the Palfrey Collection.

PLATE 20. Two bills for canal carriage of materials (Lead, Ashes, Sand) 1804-5.

PLATE 21. Interior of Wordsley Glasshouse, 1850.

frequently reported such falls, most of them occurring without warning.

The indenture of an agreement concerning the Dennis Glass-house[1] in 1728 lists the raw materials stocked on the grounds as 'Cullett, Salt Peter, Lead, Pottashes, Kelp, Sand'. As far as two at least of their raw materials, neither of which is listed, were concerned, glass-makers here were very fortunate. At their very doors they had the best 'glass-house pot clay' ever mined any-where and an abundance of coal. The clay was of such a quality that the pots could withstand even the sharply intrusive qualities of the new lead mixture. Sir Robert Mansell had learned its worth in the early days of his holding the monopoly and had sent it to his glass-houses as far north as Newcastle; later it was to become indispensable wherever glass was made. Doctor Plot (yet another member of the Royal Society) in his *Natural History of Stafford-shire*, 1686, said that this clay 'was so necessary to be had for pots that it is sent as far as London, sometimes by waggon, and sometimes by land to Beaudley and so down the Severn to Bristol and thence to London.' When William Deane and Company began bottle-making in Ireland, their first item of expenditure was £800 worth of 'Stourbridge Clay'.

The source of the sand used in the earliest days is unknown; most of the glass-houses actually stood on sand and the others within a very short distance of it; the great Western Fault of the South Staffordshire coal measures runs through the district and west of this the sand comes to the surface. Paul Tyzack the First seems to have brought his from a distance as he was fined by the Manorial Court for obstructing the highway outside his Colemans glass-house by loads of it. Later it was to come from Lynn, a difficult journey until the cutting of the canals in the late eigh-teenth century eased it.

The crude potash originally used was what the Lorrainers had traditionally used for their Waldglas; it was obtained by burning fern and bracken and sometimes heath and brushwood or even bean pods while these were still green, 'for then it is best and yields more better and white Salt . . . it must be cut in the full Growth just as it is run to seed'. Such vegetation abounded in the two Swinfords: on the Lye Waste and the Heath in Oldswinford

[1] The Dennis glass-house 'called the White house or fimbrell'; 'white' because it made the new white glass, 'fimbrell' because it stood on the 'fimbrell leasowe'; this plot of ground is mentioned in the Perambulation of the parish of Oldswinford in 1733: 'and so to the Phimbriel Leasowe at the corner of Brittle Lane'.

and in Ashwood, on Wall Heath and Pensnett Chase in Kingswinford. In the late autumn, when it had browned off dry, it was cut
and gathered by the manorial tenants for bedding their animals
during the winter months. Early in the seventeenth century, that
is, when the Lorrainers began work in the district, the Oldswinford Court Baron ordered that 'no one after this day shall burn
ffearne within this manor under penalty of forfeiting to the lord
xls' (9 October 1611). Forty shillings was the largest fine the
Court could inflict; this suggests that some glass-maker was
cutting it while still green; this is more strongly suggested by the
date in this later ordinance of the Kingswinford Court: 'that noe
person whatsoever shall burne cut or carry away any ffearne out
of Ashwood or Pensnet before the first of August'; the penalty
here was three shillings and fourpence.

Another source of potash was the Barillia imported from Spain;
according to the *Calendar of Treasury Papers* 1556–1696 'Barillia
or saffora are ashes made of a weed near Alicant and are twice
burnt and are used for the making of glass.' In 1621 James Howell,
Mansell's young manager, was buying it for his master; writing
home from Spain he describes how this 'Barillia for making
Crystall-Glasse' was extracted from 'a strange kind of Vegetable
. . . a round thick Earthy shrub that bears Berries like Barbarries
but twixt blew and green'; when these were ripe the bushes were
cut, dried, put in a pit 'a fadom deep' and burned. It was then
covered with earth; after some days the pit was again opened and
there was the 'Barillia juyce turnd to a Blew stone, so hard that it
is scarce Malleable it is sold at an hundred Crowns a Tun but I
had it for lesse.'

A third source was Kelp,[1] seaweed brought here from Scotland's
northern and Ireland's western shores where large numbers of
people were employed in preparing it. Kelp was definitely used
here in the early years of the eighteenth century: the codicil to
Thomas Henzey's will in 1712 mentions 'Ashes and Kylp' among
the items of stock at his Audnam glass-house. For window-glass
kelp was a particularly useful material for it supplied soda and
potash and lime. In addition, 'those plants that grow near the
Sea side are always the best because they acquire a great deal of
Salt by their nearness to the Sea'.

The now all-important lead, the litharge and red lead, came at
first from Derbyshire; later, in the eighteenth century, it was

---

[1] 'Kelp' according to Merret was 'principally made of that Seaplant we call
Sea-thongs or Laces'.

manufactured locally; first James Keir, F.R.S., of Holloway End Glass-house, Amblecote, set up works at Tipton then William Wheeley one at Brettell Lane opposite Jeremy Bague's glass-house and adjoining his own, for the production of red lead for the glassmen. It seems likely that when the lead came from outside the district one man was employed by the manufacturers to prepare it for their use, for the Kingswinford Parish Register in 1729 records the death of 'John Smedley ye Lead Grinder'.

The mixing of the materials, that is, the preparation of the batch, was always a specialist job. There is (and seems always to have been) a widespread notion that this proceeding is almost a carefree operation; the idea probably arose from the fact that no two manufacturers use mixtures wholly alike in materials and the proportions in which these are used. A glass-house was never a chemical laboratory; the chemist can command his conditions; he can get his desired heat to the exact degree and in an indestructible vessel from an exactly predetermined mixture produce the purest glass, and he can repeat this exactly on any occasion. Now the same heat and mixture in a glass-house would produce not glass but disaster, for it would destroy pot and furnace. The glass-maker never possessed nor could possess the chemist's perfect control. His pots differed, his furnaces varied, his temperatures were not dependable, wind direction affected them, the quality of his fuel altered them and when both wind and fuel were favourable, an inattentive teazer could spoil all. Only long experience could teach him in what proportions he must mix his ingredients in these varying conditions. Being unable to adapt his pot and furnace to a mixture of strict proportions, he had to adapt the mixture to them.[1] The use of cullet in the mixture, a normal practice, added difficulties, for the composition of this could vary considerably and could not be known, for the glass-makers would buy broken glass for cullet from any source; one of the anti-Duty petitions referred to

'many Hundreds of poor Families who keep themselves from the Parish by picking up broken Glass of all sorts to sell to the Maker'.

So the mixer, the 'founder, consore or maker of the matter and metal of the glass', was a key man. His importance, however, does

[1] 'The quantity of the Mangenese and all other colours to be put into the Fritt and metalls cannot be precisely determined either by weight or measure, but must be wholly left to the eye and judgment, tryal and experience of the Conciatore.' Neri (Merret's translation).

not seem to have been reflected in his wages in the early days: in the Earl of Cork's southern Irish glass-house while Davy the Frenchman, the gaffer, was getting three shillings a case for the window-glass he made, that is fifty-four shillings for a normal week's work, Hugh Osborne, the founder, was paid no more than seven shillings a week, to rise to eight shillings 'if I like well of him and his work'. The Kingswinford Register records the burial in 1671 of 'John Grove a founder at the glasshouse'.

If the founder was a key man, the preparation of the materials he used was a key process. The chemist can get rid of his impurities by filtration, by crystallization: but the glass-maker always knew that whatever was put in the pot came out in the glass and that the transparency of that glass betrayed every defect of quality. He had to rid his materials of all the undesirable ingredients before he filled his pot; this was particularly necessary when the crude alkalis from fern, brushwood, barillia, kelp or bean pods were used. 'The name Fritt is generally known in all Glass Houses for the first Preparation of Matter to make Glass and Crystal and which is made in the first Oven called Calcar.' Fritting, the stirring of the ingredients in a reverberatory furnace, burned off all combustible impurities and partially decomposed the rest. One of the terms of an agreement between Humfrey Batchelor and Henry Barrar concerning the Dennis glass-house in 1728 was that Barrar should leave 'a new furnace with two good spreading plates and a pott Arch and two other Arches and a CHALKER for burning'. The physical properties of the raw materials were as important as the chemical; the ingredients had to be reduced to as fine a powder as possible ('all the Art consists in reducing to impalable powder'), a difficult grinding task with bodies that were either very hard or soft and plastic. More than half of the mixture used by the broad-glass makers was sand, some of it brown with organic matter, some a dirty yellow from being mixed with loam, inevitable when digging. Washing removed the loam, sieving (fine hair sieves were used in the early years of the seventeenth century) took out the bulkier grains, fritting burned out the organic impurities.

Still more careful preliminary preparation was required of the Stourbridge glass-makers who turned to flint glass, the 'white glass-makers'. On the other hand the bottle-makers could draw on a greater variety of less pure and cheaper raw materials. The colour of their product did not concern them, and sand could go into the 'batch',[1] in fact any kind of fusible material whatever,[2] no matter how crude, for the bottle had to meet only crude requirements: enough strength to resist the pressure of its contents and the shocks of use, and chemical resistance to corrosive liquids. In some local glass-houses, however, Dennis for instance, bottles and phials were made of both kinds of glass, flint and ordinary. In a wholesale price list ('the rates and prices used by Chapmen and Dealers in a wholesale way') given in the indenture of 1728 are quoted: 'flint viols at three Shillings and sixpence for one Hundred and fifty in number. Green Viols at two shillings for one hundred and fifty.'

In 1701 that remarkable lady, Celia Fiennes, whose *Journeys* anticipated Defoe's *Tours* and Cobbett's *Rural Rides*, on her way from Wolseley to Churchill had ridden along the road through Wordsley and Amblecote:

'by the many Glass houses where they blow broad glass but they were not at work on that sort when I was there.'

When Defoe visited Worcestershire (without actually coming into the Stourbridge district) in 1724 he wrote that there was here 'a great manufacture for glass of all sorts' and mentioned 'fine flint glass' and 'glass plates';[3] glass plates could only be sheets of broad-glass.

In the next year when Humfrey Batchelor then owning and working Dennis glass-house took out an eleven-year lease of 'Lord Dudley's Glasshouse Clay Work', he was described in the indenture as 'Broadglassmaker'; broad-glass, that is, window-glass made in the Lorraine manner. The 1728 Dennis agreement refers to the products of Humfreys glass-house as 'Bottles, Viols or Bottles for Apothecaries use, Common Green Glass and Crown Glass'; crown-glass, that is, window-glass made after the Norman fashion. There is no mention of broad-glass, unless it is that

---

[1] Merret: ' "Frit" derived from Frittare to Fry.'
    'For tis nothing else but salt or ashes fryed or baked with sand and so the English call the whole quantity baked at a time in the Coker a batch.'
    The Black Country housewife used to bake small loaves which she called 'batch cakes'.
[2] The waste products of other industries were widely used for bottle-glass: slag from furnaces, ground bricks, common clay, soap-makers' waste, &c.
[3] Defoe also mentioned the local fireclay: but his geography is rather uncertain. Sir Robert Mansell had called it 'Staffordshire Clay': in 1686 Doctor Plot called it 'Amblecote Glass-house Pot Clay'.
    Defoe wrote:
    'The stone potts for the glassmakers melting their metal of which they make their fine flint glass, glass plates &c not to be found anywhere but at Stourbridge in this County' ('this County' being Worcestershire).

'Common Green Glass', which is not unlikely, broad-glass being often referred to as 'common window glass' as distinguished from 'crown-'.

This is the first record known of crown-glass being made in the Stourbridge district where for a good hundred years broad-glass had been the staple product. Crown had broken into this century-old broad-glass preserve. But the breach had been energetically resisted by the Lorrainers under the leadership of a Henzey and a Henzey house, the Dial, was to continue well into the nineteenth century producing the traditional broad-glass, the manufacture of which their ancestors had established in England in 1568.

Chapter 5

THOMAS HENZEY AND THE ENGLISHMEN

A change of fashion in window-glass brought crisis to the Stourbridge industry in the closing years of the seventeenth century; the broad-glass of the Lorrainers was being pushed out of the market by crown-glass, a Norman product. The public had taken a fancy to the bright whiteness of the new flint-glass now being made and crown offered them something of that brightness for their windows. It was the one quality in which crown excelled broad and came of the different process employed; once the bulb of metal on the crown blower's iron had been opened, the glass was not touched until it was cool and ready to be cut into quarries or panes for glazing. This meant that the natural fire surface of the glass remained unspoiled.

The gaffer spun his iron round and round much as a woman trundles a wet mop, but in his dancing hands not in the one elbow's crook; as it spun the metal spread out into a constantly thinning disc of wider and wider diameter. When this 'crown' or 'table' of glass was separated from the punty a core of thicker glass was left at the centre, the 'bull's-eye' once often to be seen in the windows of old buildings. Broad-glass making was not really the gaffer's job but his blower's; standing either on a raised platform or on floor level with a pit in front of him, he blew the paraison of glass his gatherer gave him into a long cylinder; swinging his blowpipe, he let saliva trickle into it and held his thumb over the mouthpiece to let the steam help the cylinder to grow; this was repeated until the cylinder was of the desired size. This was slit open with iron shears while still hot, laid on the marver which was sprinkled with sand and helped to flatten. The roughly rectangular sheet thus formed provided usually about four square feet of glass, the surface of which was always dulled by the tooling necessary and contact with the marver. Crown was brighter and usually much thinner than broad but broad had this advantage that there was much less waste in cutting panes from the rectangular sheet than from the circular crown.

Fashion, however, had chosen crown, and when Thomas Henzey

45

succeeded to the leadership of the Stourbridge glass industry on the death of his uncle Paul in 1693, the skies were already dark with crisis. While at work at the Henzey broad-glass house in Woolwich he had watched the threat to the traditional craft of his family developing rapidly and knew how quickly fashion spread from the capital into the provinces. Back home, he seems soon to have decided that if the family business was to survive it would have to be re-organized on a wider basis, no longer to be confined to the one product; the new flint-glass was now here to exploit, bottles offered another opportunity.

His Newcastle kinsmen, without entirely abandoning the production of broad-glass, had already turned to crown and were producing it in quantity, if not of the high quality of their broad-glass. Even by 1703, according to Neve's *Builders' Dictionary*, they were still in the apprentice stage as far as quality was concerned, for though their crown was 'most in use here in England' it was

> 'of a kind of Ash colour subject to have specks and Blemishes and streaks in it and very often warped and crooked.'

But Thomas did not turn to crown and though he led the Henzeys into the new territories of flint and bottles he did not abandon his broad-glass position but, calling in his allies, made a fight for it.

He was in his early fifties; he was well-off and had married well, but whatever substance he had was to be none too strong for all the strains it was to be called upon to stand: domestic strains, for he had fourteen children, ten of them daughters; business strains for his reorganization of the family business was not out of its first unstable stages when the Excise Duties brought it almost to a standstill.

Let us look at the Stourbridge glass scene at this time, the stage on which Thomas Henzey made a last stand for broad-glass.

It was the coming of the new 'glass of lead', 'flint glass' and not, as is generally claimed, intermarriage with the foreign glass-makers in control of the industry, that brought Englishmen into the Stourbridge glass trade.[1] Before the day of flint, only Thomas Rogers, a Welshman settled in the district, is known to have taken an active part in glassmaking and he had married into the foreign

---

[1] Other factors also contributed. Merret in his notes on Neri's text book published in 1662 wrote:

> 'Our own workmen in this Art . . . who have within these twenty years last past much improved themselves (to their own great reputation and the credit of our nation) insomuch that few foreigners of that profession are now left amongst us.'

PLATE 22.   A Richardson Chandelier.

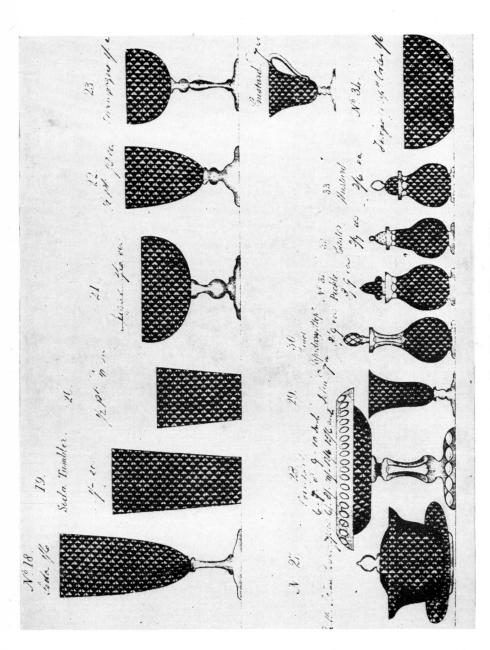

PLATE 23. Richardson Diamond Glass.

fold and taken over the Hooe house at Holloway End (Hollow-send) on the death of his Lorrainer father-in-law, Daniel Tittery. Mary Henzey, the daughter of Joshua Henzey the First, had married a Bradley, but which and whether he adopted the trade or not we do not know; he was dead by 1654 and she married the Rev. Henry Oseland who became for some time the sales manager for the broad-glass industry. It is in the last decade of the seventeenth century that we begin to hear of the first of the English glass-makers and the glass-houses they built or took over; even then the Lorrainer daughters were marrying parsons, doctors, chandlers, tanners, merchants, yeomen, gentlemen; if any married glass-makers these were kinsmen, Lorrainers themselves.

Within a few years at that century's end, strangely enough, at a time when the glass industry here, according to the glass-makers' petitions to Parliament, was staggering under the burden of the Excise Duties, the new men and glass-houses appear: the Batchelors at Dennis,[1] the Jestons at the Heath, the Bradleys first at Dennis and then at Audnam and Thomas Hamond at Brettell. King James I had wondered that 'Robin Mansell being a Sea-man whereby he hath got so much honor should fall from Water to tamper with Fire' but these substantial men saw in this second, the flint-glass, stage of the now long-established industry a rich field for commercial adventure; they did not entertain such fears as James Howell's father had done in 1621 'that this glass employment will be too brittle a foundation to build a Fortune upon'.

The first Dennis glass-house stood on 'Phimbriel Leasowe',[2] an enclosed stretch of meadow land bounded by Brettell Lane, the Stourbridge–Wolverhampton road, the Coalbourn Brook and the boundary between the manors of Amblecote and Kingswinford. In after years, when Dennis Hall was built, it became the park to that house, Dennis Park. The glass-house is named the 'Fimbrell Glasshouse' in the Batchelor-Barrar agreement of 1728. The earliest record of its existence is in a lease of 1691 by which Thomas Bradley of Oldswinford (Amblecote was in this parish at that time) glass-maker, leased a glass-house and land to Ben Batchelor, glass-maker, at an annual rent of £30.

The close connection of the Batchelors with the Henzeys suggests that they learned their trade at one of the Henzey houses in

[1] The name Dennis is a very old one; the land probably belonged to Walter le Denys (Walter the Dane) an Amblecote man who in the fourteenth century was one of the Regarders (Warders) of the Royal Forest of Kinver.

[2] This is how the name appears in the record of the Perambulation of the parish of Oldswinford in 1733.

Brettell. In 1672, Thomas and Mary Batchelor witnessed Joan Henzey's will; in 1712, their son Humfrey that of Thomas Henzey. In 1697, during the anti-Duties campaign, Elijah Batchelor ('Elisha' in the House of Commons Journals) and Ananias Henzey were giving evidence to the House of Commons 'upon the petitions of the glassmakers of Stourbridge'.

The Jestons, who seem to have built the Heath glass-house, were a substantial local family originally of Kinver; in 1578 a Thomas Jeston is named in the Court Rolls of Oldswinford as one of the ninety-four householders then living in Stourbridge town. The family had long been connected with branches of the wool trade and its members are variously described as haberdashers, bedders, clothiers and upholsterers before they became glass-makers and glass manufacturers. Roger Jeston, seeking his fortune in London, had become a citizen and member of the Haberdashers Company there; by his will in 1622, he left £6 to 'the poor of the parish and town of Kinver where I was born' besides money bequests to cousins in Hagley and Stourbridge. One of the beneficiaries was Humfrey Jeston 'of Stourbridge in co. of Stafford, son of William Jeston formerly of Burmicham[1] and late of London'. This was the Humfrey Jeston, yeoman, who was making his mark instead of writing his signature in the Oldswinford Vestry Book in 1635, was Church Warden in 1643 (the year before Joshua Henzey the First), was buying land at the Heath in 1636 and 1640 and in 1644 was petitioning Parliament for the return of three horses taken from him by the Roundheads during the Civil War.

In 1662, the Jestons had not yet abandoned wool for glass; in the Church Wardens' Accounts for that year appears this item:

'Tho: Jeston for cloth to cloathe the poor . . . 02 – 09 – 00' and in 1667 Humfrey is a 'bedder'. But by 1681, the family had become closely connected, in marriage at least, with the Henzeys; on the same day, 14 December of that year, John Jeston married Paul Henzey's daughter, Mary, and Edward Henzey Mary's cousin, Rose Jeston. John Jeston probably came to work with his father-in-law at Brettell or, living at Brettell, worked with the Bagues. In 1691, however, the Heath glass-house receives its first mention; in that year Humfrey Jeston, upholsterer, and William Jeston, his son, mortgaged

'all that new erected messuage and also all that glasshouse'

[1] Birmingham.

to Thomas Dalton, apothecary, of London. At this time, according
to the records of the London Glass Sellers' Company, the Daltons
were making bottles in their glass-house in Rosemary Lane. Then,
in 1696 and 1698, we find John Jeston giving evidence on the
effect the Excise Duties were having on the Stourbridge industry
to the House of Commons, first with John Bague and then alone;
John was then a bottle-maker. The deeds of the 1691 mortgage
refer to the newly erected house 'and all that glasshouse'; this
probably means that the glass-house had just been built, too. In
1699, a Mrs. Hunt was assessed on a glass-house at the Heath and
again in 1701; Mrs. Hunt was a Jeston; her husband was that
'Samuel Hunt, gent'[1] who, with Thomas and Robert Foley, had
built a new aisle to Oldswinford Church in 1696: he was paying
the Church Wardens in 1702 '£2 for land inclosed at the heath'.
By 1691, then, the Heath glass-house was at work.

It was in that same year that Thomas Bradley of Amblecote
leased the Dennis glass-house to the Batchelors. 'Bradley' was a
very common name in the two Swinford parishes and especially
in Kingswinford; more than one of the family's many branches
took up glassmaking and remained in the trade until well into the
nineteenth century. The Thomas Bradley who worked Dennis
was probably the son of a Thomas Bradley, 'yeoman of Oldswinford', who died intestate in 1677; letters of administration of his
estate were granted to his widow Frances and two men, one of
whom was Thomas Bradley of Oldswinford, glass-maker. After
leaving Dennis the Amblecote Bradleys may have worked for a
time with Thomas Henzey at Coalbournbrook; a 'Mr. Edward
Bradley of Colburn Brook' was buried at Kingswinford in 1716.
Later, Richard Bradley was in partnership there for a time with
John Pidcock and George Ensell, but left Amblecote to set up his
own glass-house at Wordsley; Joshua Bradley was the biggest
landowner in the Kingswinford parish; 'Edward Bradley the
Elder, white glassmaker' had bought land in Audnam, Wordsley,
in 1662 and built a glass-house on it at some time, a glass-house
which he was to sell in 1699 to John Wheeler of Wollaston Hall.
Edward, however, had three sons, Edward, Henry and Nicholas,
all white glass-makers, who probably worked the Audnam
glass-house for Wheeler. Their sister, Mary, married Thomas
Hamond, another white-glass maker; Henry married Mary James,
daughter of Winsor James, yet another Englishman making
white-glass.

[1] Witness to George Bague's Will in 1670.

Thomas Hamond was one of the Hamonds of Hall Hamond, Kinlet. A 'Thomas Hamond' appears in this district as early as in the Staffordshire Sheriff's accounts for 1640 as holding rights on Chasepool; in 1654, he appears as 'Thomas Hamond, Esq.' in the Kingswinford Court Rolls. But there is no record of a Hamond in the glass trade until 1706 when John Grove and George Bague sold 'the house in which Jeremiah Bague lately lived and now Thomas Hamond with one glasshouse' to Joseph Finch.[1] An entry in the Court Rolls in 1702 had recorded the sale of the Bague estate in Brettell to John Grove[2] of Rowley Regis, and the details reveal that there were no less than three glass-houses then at work on this land; in 1706, when the estate again changed hands, one of these houses and a dwelling-house were occupied by Thomas Hamond; the other two glass-houses and the rest of the lands passed for a time into the hands of Diana, Lady Dudley. A further entry in 1710 refers to the glass-house in the occupation of Jeremiah Bague and Thomas Hamond, glass-makers.

An entry of the previous year reveals the interesting fact that there was an inn 'known by the sign of The Glasshouse' standing by Audnam Brook on the Stourbridge–Wolverhampton road, in the occupation of Thomas Yorke.

On the number of glass-houses in the Stourbridge district at the end of the seventeenth century we have the evidence of two Houghtons: John Houghton, the Fellow of the Royal Society in his Letter No. 198, May 15, 1696, gives the number as seventeen: seven making window-glass, five bottles and five flint. Two years later, Edward Houghton, the Stourbridge glass-maker, in his evidence to the House of Commons said there were '6 or 7' white, that is flint, glass-houses and five making window-glass. Despite Edward's uncertain '6 or 7', his local knowledge should guarantee a more correct number; almost certainly the London Houghton obtained his information through correspondence and since some of the glass-houses (Dennis, for instance) were making window-

[1] The Finches were a Dudley family and their beautiful house still stands in Wolverhampton Street in that town. In 1702, Ananias Henzey sold Hawbush to Edward Finch.

Joseph Finch married Ann Bradley (widow of Edward Bradley glassmaker) formerly Ann Tittery.

Among early Worcestershire tokens was one for a halfpenny inscribed:

Obverse: John Finch of Dudley   His Halfe Peny

Reverse: in Worcestershire (Ironmongers' Arms)

[2] A Daniel Grove had married Elizabeth Henzey, daughter of John of Woolwich. The Groves later lived at the Hill, Amblecote, now the Corbett Hospital. 1724.

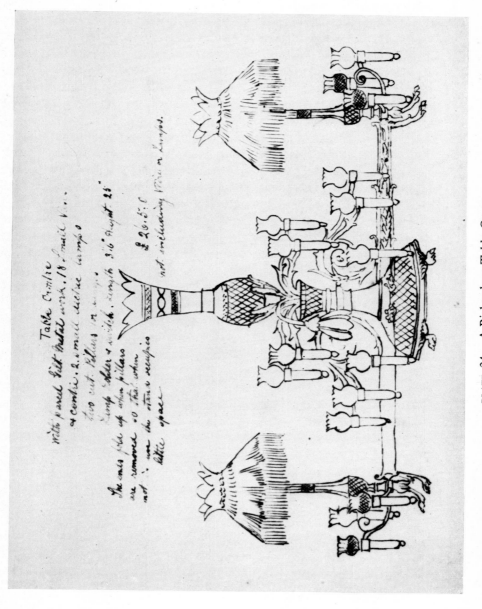

PLATE 24.   A Richardson Table Centre.

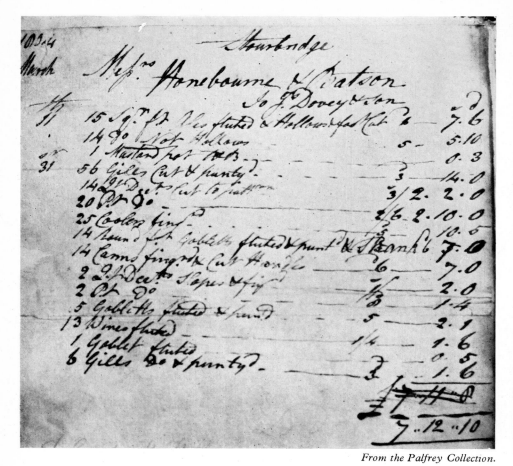

From the Palfrey Collection.

PLATE 25. Brierley Hill (Moor Lane) glass manufacturer's bill, 1804.

glass and bottles and flint, these probably appear under each of his three heads.[1]

There are three eighteenth-century lists extant: one of 1760 names ten manufacturers, a second of 1766 gives the number of glass-houses as 'about ten'; the third in 1796 gives it as eleven. As the *Gentleman's Magazine* in 1746 stated that there were then only forty glass-houses in England, whatever the exact number in the Stourbridge district, it was a quarter at the least of the national total.

It is impossible to name all of them or site them exactly; but it is certain that the following were standing, if not actually at work, in 1700: Colemans and the Heath in Oldswinford, Withymoor, Holloway End, Dennis and Coalbournbrook in Amblecote, the Bradley Audnam house in Wordsley, the two Henzey and the three Bague houses in Brettell. In addition, there was Paul Tyzack's Hagley glass-house and there may have been one or more in Dudley, for 'Wm. Trowman, glasier of Dudley' is mentioned in 1647 in the Rowley Regis Parish Register, while a later entry mentions his son, also a 'glasier' and 'glasier' at that time meant 'glass-maker'.

Of these, Colemans, Withymoor, Coalbournbrook and the two Henzey houses in Brettell were engaged almost wholly on broad-glass; the others were making bottles chiefly for the cider trade and phials for apothecaries, cruets and salts, brandy and other glasses, jelly glasses, dishes for sweetmeats, hour-glasses; that is, bottles and table-ware;[2] table-ware had been gradually coming into fashionable use. Very gradually, for though Harrison in his *Description of England* as long ago as 1586 had reported that the gentility were despising gold and silver and using Murano glasses and even the poor were contenting themselves with glasses made at home 'of fearne and burned stone'; though the Civil War demands for soldiers' pay for both armies had meant the melting down of so many gold and silver vessels, and though an Act of Parliament of 1603 had stated that glasses were then being sold by shopkeepers in all cities and towns and almost all villages in the country, Pepys in 1663 was complaining that there was nothing better than earthenware pitchers to drink from at the Lord Mayor's Banquet in the Guildhall.

[1] Edward Houghton's was propagandist Anti-Tax evidence; there was a good deal of gross exaggeration in this propaganda.
[2] Defoe in *The English Tradesman*, Vol. II, 1727, reports that watch-glasses were being made here.

Thomas Henzey had determined to stave off the final blow crown-glass was preparing to deal his broad, but he did not stake all on the hazards of this fight. In 1692 he leased Harlestones[1] Field at Coalbournbrook, Amblecote and there built a glass-house, and put his second son, John, in charge. The house was new in a very special sense, for it was here that Thomas broke with the family tradition, the broad-glass maker launched the Henzey interests into flint-glass, into bottle and vessel-making. Joshua the Third, his eldest son, was meanwhile looking after his father's London and Irish interests.

While this new venture was rocking under the buffetings of the Excise years, the old broad-glass business in London was foundering. Crown-glass had almost wholly supplanted broad in southern England and the capital and the Henzey house at Woolwich closed down for lack of orders.[2] Neve's *Dictionary* in 1703 reported that the broad-glass makers in Woolwich 'by reason they met with some Discouragement in their Proceedings there, they have laid it down for some time and do not now make there'. In the Midlands there was still some demand for it and, despite the unfavourable prospect, Thomas Henzey seems to have believed it had a future. Maybe what he heard from his kinsmen on the Continent inspired this belief, for there fortunes in the window-glass fight were moving in the opposite direction; there crown-glass was going out of fashion almost as quickly as it was taking the public's fancy here. Thomas was not to know that he was cherishing a forlorn hope, that for the next century and more crown-glass was to be 'in all but exclusive use in England', nor could he have the comfort of foreknowing that in 1778 George Ensell was to make fifty pieces of sheet-glass in the very glass-house he had just built at Coalbournbrook, and that seven of them, each measuring thirty-six inches by twenty-six, were to win the £50 premium offered by the Society for the Encouragement of Arts, Manufactures and Commerce.

In 1703, Thomas Henzey with his cousins, the Brettell Henzeys, the Tyzacks of Colemans and Withymoor and the Batchelors of Dennis on the one part and two Bristol men, father and son,

---

[1] Harlestones. This name is given in error by Grazebrook as 'Haylestones'. The Henzey house which was occupied by John Henzey, and for a time by the Rev. Henry Oseland, the Henzey sales manager, is now the offices of Webb and Corbett.

[2] It was advertised as 'to be let' in the *London Gazette*, 19 June 1701 '. . . a good wharf, Crane, Glass-house, Warehouse, Coleyard and several Out-houses thereto belonging, all in good Repair.'

merchants and glass-makers, on the other, came to an agreement concerning the manufacture and sale of broad-glass; the actual indenture of this agreement has fortunately been preserved and is in the Palfrey Collection. Professor W. H. B. Court in his *Rise of Midland Industries* 1600–1823, writing of this attempt to 'cartelize the broad-glass industry' says that, while 'it is unlikely that this was the first English cartel, it anticipates by a year or two the first recorded mention of the well-known Newcastle vend'; of the document itself he writes '(it) must be one of the most curious records of business history for its period for the boldness of its plan and precise execution of details'.

Broad-glass was being made in Bristol at the time; Neve said that 'Bristol window-glass is better than most kinds but is seldom seen in London owing to the difficulty of getting it there'. He added that 'This sort of glass which is made in Staffordshire I could never yet learn any account of, for it is a sort of Glass but seldom used in these parts of the Kingdom' (that is, London and the south). He seems not to have known that the Woolwich broad-glass house had been worked by a Staffordshire Henzey and had been producing this Staffordshire glass.

The Bristol merchants who were parties to the agreement were Benjamin Perrott the Elder of the City of Bristol gent, and Benjamin Perrott the younger his son and heir apparent';[1] they signed on their own behalf and that of their six 'servants', that is, workmen. The Perrotts were a Belbroughton family. Bristol, as the port of the Severn valley, naturally attracted many of the venturesome in trade from that valley, like the Foleys and the Dolmans; its glass industry also drew glass-makers, like the Littles and the Bradleys, from the Stourbridge district. In 1691, we hear of John Little, an Amblecote glass-maker, apprenticing sons of his there;[2] the Littles later founded a very successful glass-making business in the city and a Kingswinford Bradley built the Temple Backs Glass-house there. The Perrotts were interested in both trade and glass-making.

The agreement is dated 1 May 1703 and was to last for eleven

---

[1] Two Perrotts in 1586 married two James daughters whose mother was a Lyttelton. John's signature often appears in the Oldswinford Vestry Book in the early seventeenth century. In 1625 Humfrey was fined £12 10s. for refusing knighthood at Charles I's coronation. In 1691 John Perrott of Bristol, son of Henry Perrott of Bell Hall, bought Pedmore Hall. John became High Sheriff in 1720; he gave a silver chalice to Pedmore Church—*Gloria Deo—Ex dono Johannis Perrott Armiger.*

[2] One to 'John Perrott glassmaker of Bristol'.

years; by its terms the Perrotts were neither to make broad-glass themselves nor to promote its manufacture by any others than the broad-glass makers signing the agreement save in London or 'within ten miles of London stone'. These glass-makers were to deliver at Wribbenhall or Bewdley (that is, for river carriage to Bristol) eight score cases a year of 'merchantable uncut Broad-glass'. If any broad-glass house other than theirs was set up within forty miles of either Bristol or Stourbridge, the agreement would become void. If it became thus void the glass-makers were to furnish the Perrotts with

> 'such & so many able & sufficient workmen blowers & Gatherers to make broad glass in the City of Bristoll or in any other place within ffifteen miles of the same city as shall be sufficient & they shall have occasion for to carry on manage & supply the work of one broad glass house at for & after the wages & rates of thirty shillings p. week for each Master Workman ffifteen shillings p. week for each Blower & ten shillings p. week for each Gatherer whilst they respectively work.'

The umpires chosen to arbitrate in any differences which might arise were 'John Perrott of Pedmore Gent and Edward Hallen of Stourbridge Writingmaster'.[1]

If this agreement were carried out what would it mean? The normal output of a broad-glass house working its forty weeks a year was 720 cases; the four concerned in the agreement could therefore put on the market 2880 cases a year; of these the Perrotts guaranteed to take no more than 160, one out of every eighteen cases produced.

Forty years previously, in 1663, Robert Foley, the Stourbridge merchant who became official Ironmonger to the Royal Navy in 1660, had, in partnership with Joshua Henzey the Second, come to an agreement with the broad-glass makers of three of these houses, Colemans, the Hooe and Brettell, to take their entire output of broad-glass for a year 'at twenty shillings by the case'. If no other glass-house was set up within eighty miles of Withymore within that year, then the agreement was to continue for a further two years. Unfortunately the indenture of this agreement has not survived; its details are known from their being disclosed in evidence given in a lawsuit in the years 1667 and 1668. In 1660 Foley had bought 648 cases from the Colemans 'chair' alone, when it was temporarily working at Chelwood.

[1] In 1705 Edward Hallen was with Thomas Dalton in temporary occupation of the Heath glasshouse.

PLATE 26.   Joshua Hodgetts, Engraver.

(a)

PLATE 27. (a) Engraving Shop at Moor Lane, late nineteenth
century. (b) Cutting Shop at Moor Lane, late
nineteenth century.

(b)

But fashion was to prove stronger than any cartel; for some years the 1703 agreement succeeded in maintaining the price of broad-glass at 26s. the case, yet soon there was little demand for it at any price. The *London Gazette* told the story of the breakdown of the industry in a series of advertisements which were really obituary notices; unemployment grew:

'1710. 27 July.

Whereas several experienced and able workmen in the making of broad glass now inhabiting in the parish of Old-swinford are willing to be partners or to work as journeymen at reasonable rates in any broad glasshouse within the Kingdom of Great Britain. If any person shall think fit to join with them in any partnership or to employ them as journeymen they are desired to send word to Mr. Thomas Fryer at the sign of the Crown in Stourbridge.'

Workmen these, not blowers or gatherers, gaffers out of work; but not Henzeys yet: they patronized the 'Talbot' not the 'Crown' (ominous name). Thomas had been admitted to the Talbot Club in December 1702. Next, cut prices to shore up the cracking structure:

'1712. 10 January.

Whereas the price of Broad Glass or Window Glass in and about Stourbridge for many years has been 26s. the case. Now all Glaziers and others are desired to take notice that from this time the said Broad Glass or Window Glass will be sold by any of the Broadglass-makers thereabouts at 22s. the case either broad or cut.'

By the end of 1716, the price was down to 18s. a case. In January 1717, the three Henzey brothers of the second Brettell House broke away from the rest of the broad-glass makers; again the *London Gazette* is the mouthpiece of this melancholy announcement:

'Whereas Broad Glass hath been lately sold at 18s. per case at the Glasshouse near Stourbridge, there is now Broad Glass to be sold at 16s. per case[1] by Paul Henzey, John Henzey and Joseph Henzey at their Glasshouse in Brettle Lane near Stourbridge aforesaid. And when broad glass is raised in price due notice shall be given in the Gazette.'

---

[1] Among the 'Reasons against Mansel's Patent' given to Parliament on 16 April 1624 appears this:
  'if every Artist had a free liberty to make Glasse . . . window-glasse would be sold for 16/- the Case that is now sold for 22/6.'

That notice was not given either in the *Gazette* or elsewhere; instead, Thomas Milward noted in his daybook that in April of the same year he had bought forty cases of broad-glass from Zachariah Tyzack at 14*s*. 6*d*. a case. When John Henzey died at Harlestones in the same year he had fifty cases in stock. Unemployment brought bankruptcies in its dismal train, the last throes of the dying industry: in 1721, the *Gazette* announced, instead of a rise in price, the failure of William Andrews of Brettell, broad-glass maker, in 1723 Samuel Tyzack of Kingswinford and Benjamin Batch of Amblecote glass-makers both, came to grief.

But the Henzeys did not fail:[1] Thomas Henzey's foresight and vigour had put them firmly on new feet. He had built Coalbournbrook for his son John who was there producing flint-glass; in 1704, he erected that glass-house which came to be called 'The Dial' on a piece of land in Audnam bounded by the Wolverhampton–Stourbridge road and Brettell Lane; shortly afterwards in Amblecote, not many yards away, on meadow-land between the Stourbridge Road and the river Stour, he set up the Platts bottle-house for Joshua.

Now, whatever happened to broad-glass, the Henzeys were still secure in the glass world, they would remain glass-makers. However, despite the close attentions his new ventures demanded, Thomas did not wholly abandon his old trade. Sceptical of the omens of the window-glass market and strong in his belief that sooner or later broad-glass would return to favour, he still made it at the Dial; the new house became a kind of asylum for a decaying craft to be cherished and kept alive as long as possible. In the event, though Thomas could not know this, broad-glass making was actually practised here until its natural successor, sheet-glass, was being produced in this district. In 1761, broad-glass makers were still being advertised for to work there; in 1774, Elijah Patchett, innkeeper of 'Jacob's Well' in Audnam, blew his cylinders, slit and opened them into sheets of the old broad at the Dial. In 1778, George Ensell won the Society of Arts' premium for sheet-glass and by 1780 he and Robert Honeyborne 'had established a manufactory of German sheet and crown glass' at Brierley Hill.

Thomas Henzey died suddenly in 1712; he had made a will in 1709 by which, after generous bequests in money and household goods to his six living daughters, he left his Dial interests ('Glasshouse, outbuildings, furnaces, tools, stock of Glass, debts,

[1] The Perrotts soon turned to 'crown' themselves.

PLATE 28. Glass-makers' friggers.

PLATE 29. Glass-manufacturers' friggers : the Dennis 'Cannon'.

ashes, kelp and the remainder of the lease') equally between his three sons, Joshua, John and Edward, 'on condition that they become Executors': he made special provision for his youngest son, Benjamin.

One morning late in April, 1712, he appeared at the house of Thomas Milward, his attorney, at an early hour and announced his wish to alter his will there and then. Milward, who was on the point of setting out on a business journey which would keep him away from home for three days and 'seeing Henzey then in health', begged to be excused and promised to deal with the matter immediately he returned. He was too late: Thomas Henzey had died in the afternoon of the day Milward returned, but in his businesslike way he had written his instructions to Milward on a paper which John had found 'in the Closet of his father'.

Since 1709, two family happenings had troubled Thomas: four of his daughters had married well into English families, Frances was still unwed, but Mary, against her father's wishes, had married her cousin, Paul Henzey, and Edward, his third son, despite his long training in the craft, had abandoned glass-making and become a maltster. His disappointments did not embitter Thomas but they hurt him; so in the codicil to his will, as which the note that John had discovered was recognized by the whole family (with Milward and Humfrey Batchelor in attendance), Edward was not to be an executor and, instead of the £200 of the will, Mary was to get only the interest—the 'principall to be secured for her children if any'.

Thomas Henzey's eldest son, Joshua the Third, was to be the last Henzey in the Stourbridge district. We know little of his early years save that he was trained in the family craft, 'he hath been bred to and doth well understand the Trade and Mistery of makeing broad glass', probably at the Woolwich house. The date of his returning to settle in this district suggests that the Henzey glass-house at Woolwich was closed down in 1700. In that year he married; like the first Joshua he took to wife a woman very much his senior, Elizabeth Henzey,[1] the widow of Paul Henzey of Hawbush, his father's cousin. The marriage brought with it that third share in the second Brettell glass-house which had been Paul Henzey's, with 'one third part of the ready money goods

---

[1] 'Paul Henzey married Elizabeth from Enfield named Cranwell from a house standing by a tall fir tree and near to the place where Lady Dorothy Grey has built an Almshouse.' Enfield is Enville. Joshua was ten years old at the time of this marriage.

wares Stock and moneys owing'. Joshua went to live with Elizabeth in the house attached to the works of which Paul had been manager. His two working partners[1] were Paul's brother Ananias and Joshua's uncle Edward Henzey the Elder, both considerably older men than Joshua. From the first they were at variance; we know how unreliable Ananias was and what grief his deceit had brought to his father's last days; Edward seems to have resented what he considered the younger man's intrusion. Together, the two older men put every obstacle in his way even to the extent 'of causing the workeing fire in the Glass house to be putt out on purpose to hinder him working there'. They challenged every right he claimed; it had been the rule in Paul's day

> 'that upon the first monday in every month there should be monthly Accounts made in writeing concerning the said trade or partnershipp and the Effects and Concernes thereof for the next month.'

They denied that any such accounts were kept and, if they were, Joshua's right to see them.

The fact that the three partners were making broad-glass probably accounts for Joshua's perseverance for at least twelve years in these harassing conditions; he shared his father's enthusiasm for the old craft and supported his fight for its survival. All three signed the 1703 agreement with the Perrotts and continued producing broad-glass until, at least, 1712, when Thomas Henzey died. In the same year Edward Henzey retired; in the same year, too, the price of broad-glass fell from 26s. to 22s. a case. Joshua had now to supervise work at the Dial and the Platts in addition to Brettell; he probably handed over the management of the Brettell house to Ananias.

And Ananias failed him; shortly after Lady Day 1713, without notice, he walked out, 'absented himself and the work stood'; Joshua was then 'the only sufficient man' left. Despite his heavy responsibilities, he kept the glass-house going for a further year or two, when the three sons of Ananias, Paul, John and Joseph, took over; these were the Henzeys who broke away from the Association of broad-glass makers in 1717 and advertised their glass at 16s. the case while the others were charging 18s.

On 2 December 1710, Thomas Milward, the attorney[2] who

---

[1] There were also two sleeping partners: Richard Hickman, a Stourbridge clothier, and Thomas Tyrer.

[2] At Milward's funeral in 1724 the following glass-makers were mourners: Winsor James, Edward Henzey, Joshua Henzey, Humfrey Batchelor.

served the Henzeys (and other glass-makers) and traded in fireclay, made out a personal balance sheet[1] in which the following items appear:

'Debtor.

To severall persons for money at Interest	
Mrs. Tho: Henzey	060:00:00
Mr. Bigoe Henzeys Acct for mony recd for him	14:00:00
Mrs. Joan Henzey	12:18:00
Thos Milward is Creditor now in Good Debts for money laid out & business done	
Mr. Thos & John Henzey	3s. 4d.
Tyzack of Hagley	4/-
Mr. Josh Henzey on Birth of his next child by any other wife	16:2:6.'

The three items on the debit side reflect the substantial standing of the Henzeys: Thomas's wife's £60 of interest; Bigoe's rents—Bigoe, landed gentleman and glass-maker of Barnagrothy, King's County, Ireland, and owner of the second Brettell Henzey glass-house; Joan's interest—Joan, posthumous and spinster daughter of John Henzey of Woolwich and Hawbush, who had left her ('the child my wife Mary goeth with'), co-heiress with his other children and £200 in money.

The last and most important item at this point throws light on Joshua's domestic cares, on a matter which probably caused him more anxiety than either the unkindly behaviour of his uncle-partners or the decline of broad-glass, on which the fortunes of the family were no longer wholly dependent. This was the prospect that in the Stourbridge district at least the Henzey name would disappear, a most unpleasant prospect for a member of an ancient and noble family.

Of Thomas Henzey's four sons, two, Edward and Benjamin, were unmarried; of the second son John's children only three daughters survived and John himself died in 1717. Joshua himself was childless. His first wife, Elizabeth, died in 1715 and was

---

Samuel Whyle, gent. had been 'employed as an Attorney Sollicitor and agent' for the earlier Henzeys. Whyle had built Pedmore Hall (sold to the Perrotts later) and 'planted the Orchyards about it being fourty Acres at least'. 'He was a Pious Hospitable Ingenious Generous and learned Gentleman.' He died in London in 1683 and was buried 'under the Chappel in Lyncolns Inn'. He was one of the patrons whose generosity enabled Captain Andrew Yarranton to make his tour of industrial inquiry on the Continent.

[1] In the Palfrey Collection.

buried at Kingswinford with her first husband, Paul;[1] he then married Bridget Thompson, sister of a Banbury doctor. The children of his Henzey cousins in the Stourbridge district were daughters, too, save one, John, son of that John who with his brothers worked the second Brettell glass-house; but while on a visit to their kinsmen in Newcastle, both Johns, father and son, were drowned while crossing the Tyne. The exact implication of that last credit item is difficult to understand: Joshua's 'next child' would have been his first. Elizabeth, his first wife, had still five years to live, but neither Milward nor Joshua could count on her not outliving her husband. In fact, he survived both her and her childless successor. However, Joshua's anxiety is implicit in it. What he feared actually came to pass; fifty years later, though it was then true to say that if one scratched almost any man of standing in the district one found a Henzey the name appeared only as a Christian name. Joshua the Third was the last of the Henzeys.

We know very little of Joshua's last years; he left the Brettell dwelling-house for the Platts, probably on his second marriage. John of Harlestones had died in 1717, a well-to-do English gentleman owning lands in 'Castle Morton, Birch Morton, Longdon, Kingswinford and elsewhere in the counties of Worcester and Stafford', a twelve-roomed house in Amblecote, £223 of ready money in his coffer, 132 ounces of plate and 'debts due' of £860; a glass-maker with a stock of fifty cases of broad-glass. Edward died in 1725; in his will he called himself 'broadglassmaker' but then referred to 'the business of a Malster which I now follow'; after more or less token bequests to his brothers and sisters amounting in all to £160, he left his house and belongings to an Edward Piddock,[2]

> 'the Boy that now lives with me whose Maintenance and
> Education I have for several years taken care of . . .'

His malting business was to be carried on for Edward's benefit by Edward himself and 'Elizabeth Westwood spinster my servant'. In 1730, Benjamin died and Joshua was left to carry on alone; two years later, he buried Bridget his second wife at Kingswinford. On whom was the Henzey mantle now to fall?

Joshua chose one of his few nephews, the son of his sister Elizabeth who had married William Pidcock of Ashbourne. Joshua

[1] Paul's grave is in Kingswinford churchyard on the right-hand going into the church near the porch.

[2] PIDDOCK. Joshua's adopted nephew was John PIDCOCK. This close similarity of names has caused some confusion. Edward's adopted heir appears as 'Edward Piddock alias Henzey' in the Kingswinford Parish Register.

PLATE 30.   Glass-manufacturers' friggers :
A Stevens and Williams whiskey bottle.

By courtesy of Thomas Webb & Sons.

PLATE 31.   A Dennis vase ; traditional cutting.

died in 1737, and left £2000 in money bequests to his sisters, nephews and nieces; the rest of his estate went to John Pidcock whom he had made his sole executor.

Joshua had other financial interests in the glass industry. In 1725 he had come to the help of the Bradleys' Audnam glass-house: the business here had long been trembling on the brink of bankruptcy. Jeremiah Rogers of the Holloway End glass-house, Thomas Hamond, Winsor James, all glass-makers, and Joseph Finch, ironmonger, and John Gibbons, saddler, had all been concerned in a complicated series of agreements concerning this business. By 1733, Joshua was owed the substantial sum of £479 10s. 7d.: he sold his rights in the business to 'John Ward of Sedgley Park, Esq.' who was to become Lord Ward in 1740. Henry Bradley, son of the founder Edward Bradley and son-in-law of Winsor James, was

> 'the real owner who can get possession from J. Ward for £500 paid in six months.'

By 1727 he was bankrupt: his son Henry was glass-making at St. Dunstan's, Stepney, in 1770.[1]

The last of the Henzeys left this a glass-busy district. The industry had been for many years a wholly English institution, whatever foreign names the makers bore, and now the names, too, were English. The footing of the new English entrants into the glass world, however, was for long far from secure; the decline of broad-glass shook the Henzeys, but none of the Englishmen, save the Batchelors, were even nominally broad-glass makers.

The Henzey Brettell houses fell on evil times; the triumph of crown-glass seems to have killed the first one outright; the death of the second was a more protracted affair. In 1724 it came into the hands of one of the financially unfortunate or unpractical members of the Compson family of Wordsley, a Burlton Compson of Burton-on-Trent, a businessman's not a glass-maker's speculation; his only previous connection with glass-making was purely a personal one through a John Burlton who had married one of the daughters of Paul Tyzack the First, and the experience of two of his relatives, James and Thomas Compson, had no lesson for him; in the previous year, 1723, a 'Commission of Bankruptcy under the Great Seal of Great Britain' had been awarded against them

---

[1] 'Joshua Henzey of Audnam of the parish of Kingswinford' who was holding a mortgage of £120 on houses in 'Crown Lane, Stowerbridge', in 1726 lent a further £40. In the Palfrey Collection is a receipt for £43 signed by Joshua, interest on this mortgage.

and their glass-house on Dob Hill, Wordsley, had been sold to
Winsor James.[1] Colemans and Withymore, too, seem to have
closed down. Indeed, save for the Dial, no house was making
broad-glass and there is no record of any of the oldest glass-
houses being at work at all except Holloway End where the
Rogers, 'white glassmakers', were now producing tableware. In
the Palfrey Collection the following appears:

'19 Feb. 1717.

Received of mr. John ffoley six shillings being in full for a
parsell of Glases

Thos Rogers.'

Bankruptcy had also disturbed production at the Bague glass-
houses, save for the one worked by Thomas Hamond, as occupier
not owner, in which he continued producing his white-glasswares;
successfully, too, for he was gradually buying up lands until he
became one of the largest landowners in the Kingswinford parish.
In 1717, Joseph Finch had sold the house to a Dudley baker who
mortgaged it in the next year to William Seager of the 'Red Lyon
in Brettle'.

The details of Hamond's purchases of land tell the story of the
entry of another important white-glass maker, Robert Honeyborne, and the further strengthening of the position of John
Pidcock. The Kingswinford Court Rolls record the surrender of
land to 'Thomas Hamond and his wife Maria and after their deaths
to Anne Hamond their daughter'. Anne married Robert Honeyborne and bore him two children before her death in her twentieth
year; Hamond, a son who died before he was three years old, and
Maria. Subsequent entries, from 1728 onwards, read '. . . to
Thomas Hamond and after his death to Maria Honeyborne daughter of Robert Honeyborne and heiress of Thomas Hamond';
Maria, Hamond heiress, married John Pidcock, Henzey heir.

Robert Honeyborne joined his father-in-law in his prosperous
Brettell house; his success, too, is reflected in the Court Rolls,
Robert, like Hamond, buying wide lands in the parish. One such
entry is particularly important: on 16 November 1732, Honeyborne bought from the Bradleys several pieces of land

'existing at or near the place called Moor Lane'

and the house there in which he was living at the time. There is

---

[1] In 1798, another Compson, John, 'now a debtor in his Majesty's Gaol at
Newgate in the City of London, Tailor' was surrendering lands by letter of
attorney. The letter was witnessed by 'John Kirby, Keeper of Newgate'.
John's attorney was 'John Compson of the Hill top of Belbroughton Gent'.

PLATE 32.   A Dennis bowl ;   traditional cutting.

By courtesy of Stuart & Sons Ltd.

PLATE 33.   Pieces designed by Ludwig Kny (son of F. E. Kny).

as yet no mention of a glass-house, but this was the site on which the glass-house was built which was the original home of 'Stevens and Williams'.

The Jestons at the Heath made little success of their new glass-house; as we have seen they had mortgaged it in 1705 to Thomas Dalton, who later came into possession. In 1709, he re-leased it to John Jeston, a glass-maker not an upholsterer, and son-in-law to Paul Henzey. The Jestons again took over but by 1727 they were mortgaging it again; seven years later Humphrey Jeston, 'glass manufacturer of the Heath', was bankrupt and the Commissioners worked the house until 1736 when it was put up for sale under the careless misnomer, 'Heath's New Glasshouse'.[1]

The Bradleys were no more successful at their Audnam glass-house, and of the three brothers who had worked it Edward broke away and set up on his own next door in 1716. In 1727 Henry became bankrupt; Edward kept his head above the always threatening waves of insolvency until 1743 when he too sank.

At Dennis the Batchelors seem to have sailed a smoother course than most of the early English glassmen; though they described themselves as 'broadglassmakers', as a result of their training with the Henzeys, they had no sentimental or other regard for the old glass and welcomed its successful rival; they made bottles and tableware in flint and ordinary glass besides crown window-glass.[2]

In 1728, Humphrey Batchelor took a partner in Henry Barrar, another Amblecote glass-maker; there was already or was soon to be a close family connection between the two families; where Barrar had formerly worked is not known. The Batchelor-Barrar agreement contains some curious articles; it was for a fixed term of fourteen years at the end of which Barrar was 'to leave a new furnace with two good spreading plates[3] and a pott Arch and two other Arches with all the Doors and Windows in good repair and a Chalker for burning'. He was to take over the whole stock of 'flint Glass Viols and Glasswares', the raw materials, 'Cullett Salt Peter Lead Potashes Kelp and Sand' all the 'whole Potts

---

[1] The 1796 list gives the name of the firm 'Russell & Heath'. An 1818 Directory states that the Dial was run by 'Pidcock Cope & Broad', the 'broad' having strayed from the products '(broad)glass and bottles'.

[2] It has been suggested that the 'Ben Batch, glassmaker of Amblecote' advertised as an insolvent debtor in 1723 was Ben Batchelor. 'Batch' is a phonetic spelling of 'Bache', a common name in the district. During the Civil War a William Bache was complaining to Parliament that its soldiers had robbed him. In 1732, a Ben Batchelor had a glass-house at Broseley, Salop.

[3] For flattening broad-glass.

and Pott bottoms and alsoe all pipes Implements and Tools whatsoever made use of or made for working or making of white Glass Glass Viols or any other Sort of Glass or Glassware'; for these he was to pay

'one moiety or Equal half part of all the money'
the amount to be decided on by agreement and based on

'the rates and prices the Chapmen and Dealers in a wholesale way'
were paying. The indenture[1] contains a comprehensive price list of all kinds of ware in stock:

'flint Glasses, flint crewetts, ordinary glass Crewets and Salts, flint Viols, green Viols, Double Brandy Glasses, flint Brandy Glasses and Jelly Glasses.'

While Barrar held the glass-house 'of and under Humfrey Batchelor' he was to employ Batchelor's smith to mend the glass-makers' tools and pay Batchelor for his services at the rate of four shillings a week for every six workmen so served; he was further to pay five shillings for every dozen bottles and ten shillings for every case of 'Common Green or Crown' made and he was to make no more than twenty-dozen phials a week.

Batchelor, on the other hand, was to pay Barrar two shillings and sixpence 'out of every pound sterling' of the value of 'the several sorts of Glasses and Viols' produced and one shilling for every pound weight of white glass.

Maybe Humphrey Batchelor was finding his new business—the mining of clay

'such as is and for the space of one and twenty years last past has been commonly used for makeing of Glasshouse pots and Glasshouse Bricks and Iron furnaces'
had captured all his commercial enthusiasm and he had called in Barrar as a sort of managing director. It was in 1725, three years before his arrangement with Barrar that he had taken an eleven-year lease of

'all that clayworke lying & being in Pensnett[2] & Amblecoat in the parish of Kingswinford called or known by the name of Lord Dudleys Glasshouse Clay Worke.'
Lord Edward Dudley's 'space of one and twenty years last past' was a rare understatement. Exactly a hundred years previously Sir Robert Mansell, the monopolist, was telling the Parliament of King James I that a few years earlier

[1] The Indenture is in the Palfrey Collection.
[2] Pensnett, the common name then for Pensnett Chase.

'no clay could be by any means had to make pots nearer than the County of Stafford from whence it was brought to New Castle at an infinite charge'

and again in 1686, Doctor Robert Plot, 'Professor of Chymistry in the University of Oxford' was writing in his *Natural History of Staffordshire*:

'the Clay that surpasses all others . . . is that at Amblecoat . . . of a dark blewish colour whereof they make the best pots for the Glasshouses of any in England . . . so very good is it for this purpose and so very necessary to be had that it is sent as far as London, sometimes by Waggon, and sometimes by Land to Beaudley and so down the Severn to Bristol and thence to London.'

The clay lay below

'land called Ravensitch Coppice in the thornes in Pensnet Chase on the south side of the way leading from Amblecote lane End to Cradley fforge.'[1]

This land had been previously leased (1709) to John Bowles of Kidderminster who paid

'£100 per annum and one hundred and twenty Quarts of good sound marketable merchantable and well-condicioned wine (to witt) Sixty Quarts of white wine and Sixty Quarts of Clarret Wine with glass bottles to contain the same on 25 December to be delivered yearly at the Talbott Inn in Stowerbridge.'

Payment of rent in such pleasant kind was replaced in Batchelor's agreement by a royalty of six shillings

'for each Tun of Clay, each Tun 18 sacks of the same sise as now are and for seaven years last past have been used to carry Clay and no larger and which weigh two and twenty hundred weight.'

Bowles was to take no more than 425 tons a year; Batchelor could get all he could sell but this only to customers outside the Stourbridge district; this hungry local market Lord Dudley reserved to himself:

'to sell Clay for making potts to melt mettle in or for Glasshouse bricks to the Glassmakers in and about Stowerbridge to be used within ten miles of the said Clayworke.'[2]

---

[1] This road is still called 'The Thorns' and clay is still worked on this land.

[2] When Paul Henzey leased part of this land from 'Humble Warde of Hymley Esq' (Lord Ward) his agreement also contained this reservation, 'alsoe all clay for to make glasse be excepted unto Humble Warde'. 1654.

As further security to his own profitable closed Stourbridge market (and incidentally at least to Batchelor's) the noble clay-owner imposed this second condition: Batchelor was to pay

'half such sum as Lord Dudley shall pay Mister Dudley Brettle in order to lett his Claymine lye still & ungot the better to encourage the sale of the clay let to Humphrey Batchelor'.

A few years later this clay was being exported to Ireland[1] in casks instead of sacks, each cask holding half a ton; in the early nineteenth century its price was £4 15s. 6d. per ton; by this time it was being sent out to all parts of the world having proved its

'peculiar excellency that a pot made of it with a proper heat will melt almost anything into glass.'

A large proportion of this exported clay went by coast-wise traffic from Bristol; in 1714, the Milwards of Wollescote, also exploiting the strictly confined resources of this clay, made an agreement with George Knight of Bewdley, who was engaged in this Bristol trade; Knight agreed to take the output of the Milward claypits for three years but left them the lucrative privilege of supplying glass, iron and brass works within three miles of Stourbridge. Knight was to pay £16 2s. 6d. per year and sixty quart bottles of cider.

[1] Christopher Merret's notes to Neri's *Art of Glass*, 1662, referring to London glass-makers:

'Pots made of clay fetched from Purbeck in the Isle of Wight, the very same which makes Tobacco pipes. Those for Green Glass are made of Non-such clay, mixed with another clay brought from Worcestershire which bears the fire better than that of Non-such but both together make the best pots.'

PLATE 34.   Air Twist Wine Service.

PLATE 35.   Jug and stemmed goblet, *circa* 1850.   Ruby cased on
crystal : decoration engraved through ruby.

Chapter 6

THE SEVENTEENTH-CENTURY SCENE

The Lorrainers of Newcastle upon Tyne, Henzeys, Tyzacks and Titterys as here, for long kept themselves so tightly closed a community that they were called 'The Strangers'.[1] They were following a centuries-old family tradition born of the desire and intent to preserve the secrets of their craft. The Lorrainers of the Stourbridge district threw their gates wide open to association of all kinds with the native families among whom they had come uninvited. Fortunately they did not come as industrial rivals, for commercial rivalry in the early seventeenth century was as often as not expressed in personal violence: Dud Dudley had his furnaces wrecked; Mrs. Lyttelton's 'overseer of woods' threw down the Halesowen ironmaster Humfrey Lowe's hearths in Uffmore; Walter Stanley, no low-born ruffian but 'a man of very great living wealth and countenance', broke down the dam that served Thomas Parkes's forge at West Bromwich; Parkes himself with thirty of his workmen 'armed with pikes swords and daggers' invaded the mill 'belonging to William Whorwood of Sandwell Hall' (cousin to the Whorwoods of Stourton Castle) and drove out his men; Whorwood retaliated by beating up Parkes's men, dismantling his forge and actually carting away the plant and tools to Sandwell Hall.

And one of the prime causes of the Lorrainers' abandoning the Sussex Weald had been the threats of fire and slaughter with which the native ironworkers had assailed them; but there they had been foreigners making demands on that diminishing supply of timber which was the lifeblood of the English industry. Here no such clash could occur; there was coal for all and to spare, coal under their very furnaces; nor were they trade rivals; they had

---

[1] As late as 1710 at Newcastle
    'permission was given by the Common Council to the glassmakers to erect at their own charge a gallery at the west end of St. Anne's Chapel for their own use'.
In the sixteenth century a licence from the Bishop had empowered them to hold their meetings for private worship at fixed times. In the Stourbridge district the Lorrainers joined with the English worshippers from the first.

brought a new and welcome industry, their window-glass would satisfy a growing local demand, their domestic ware fitted a new table fashion.

When they arrived they seem to have doffed their traditional exclusiveness on the threshold as a visitor might his cloak and hat and to their novel sociability the local families of substance responded with friendliness. The Addenbrooks, iron and coal men, had no hesitation in leasing coal-bearing land to a Tyzack and the Brettell family did not forbid two of its members to marry Henzeys. The district was then one of the busiest industrial areas of the kingdom: coal-mining and iron manufacture had been carried on here for centuries and new technical methods had been introduced immediately they were known; Lord Dudley had built one of the new blast-furnaces on Pensnett Chase, the Lowes one at Halesowen; Richard Foley had set up a slitting-mill at Kinver, Dud Dudley had used pit-coal to smelt his ores; the valleys of the Stour and its tributary, the Smestow, housed more mills than any other equal length of water-course in the country and the waters of these streams ran into the Severn, then one of the busiest rivers in Europe.

In these thriving industries most of the local men of substance naturally took an active part and they did not confine themselves to the carrying on of already established trades: they encouraged new ones. For instance, even the 'ingenious (English) gentleman' could not yet make a practicable tin-plate such as we had then to import from the continent; he could neither roll an iron plate thin enough nor spread the tin equally on what he could roll. When Captain Andrew Yarranton, Civil War veteran, local magistrate who occasionally sat at the 'Cock Inn', Stourbridge, to take evidence of witnesses in lawsuits, and ironmaster[1] announced that he was willing to tour the continent and discover the secrets of the trade if somebody would finance him, he soon found willing patrons; ten 'noble patriots' he dubbed them, six of whom were of this district, Thomas and Phillip Foley, Joseph Newbrook, Samuel Whyle, Nicholas Baker and John Finch.

It was with such men as these and their families, that the Lorrainers hobnobbed; they married with them, worshipped with them, bought and sold with them, clubbed, drank, played and dined with them; and this, despite the fact that, while the Englishmen

---

[1] It has been claimed on the strength of some of his proposals, such as the 'Land Bank', and writings, that Yarranton was the founder of political economy.

were mostly business men, financing and directing concerns without actually practising the craft, the Lorrainers were work-men, sweating through their six-hour shifts,

> 'compell'd to work in their shirts like Cyclopes with a straw broad-brim'd Hat on their heads to defend their eyes from excedency of heat and light'.[1]

Not all of these men had made, or were to make, fortunes like the Foleys, who jumped in two generations from their slitting-mill into the House of Lords and set up their sons on such separate and splendid estates as Witley Court, Stoke Edith and Prestwood, the Rogers who went from bottles to bullion and became London bankers, the Knights, the Crowleys; but most of them prospered into a securely comfortable family future. Many of them, without abandoning their original ventures, came to dabble in glass as a subsidiary source of income.

During the Great Civil War, the district was a no-man's-land in the holding of neither party for long, but plagued and systema-tically plundered by both; as far as we know, the glassmen worked steadily through it and, like the other householders paid their 'weekly pay' to the constable whose duty it was to collect it for the wages of whatever troop was in temporary occupation and suffered the forced company of such soldiers as were billeted on them. If the troopers' swords were unfleshed here, their thieving hands were busy enough: Humfrey Jeston lost three of his horses, William Bache of Amblecote was robbed of his money and writings, Paul Tyzack too lost his 'writeings[2] which were imbezeled and taken from him by they souldyers.'

Meanwhile the Foleys were doing well out of munitions. The colliers and nailers who seized Dudley Castle to hold it for the King 'took some ironworks of Master Foleys where it is said they are casting of ordnance and making iron bullets'; when Sir William Brereton captured Wolverhampton for Parliament, he took as part of his spoil 'some cannon bulleits from Mr. Folies forges and the moulds which made these bulleits which were

---

[1] The *Newcastle Chronicle* reported on 18 March 1769 the death of Mr. Joshua Henzell in his eighty-second year. 'Though he was esteemed the most corpulent person in this part of the country yet (till within a few years of his latter end) he always displayed himself in the manual execution of his business, a glassmaker, as possessing the abilities of an able workman united with the alacrity of youth and has thereby acquired a very handsome fortune.'

[2] Paul's writings (and William Bache's) were his deeds &c; among those lost was the indenture of his nephew Zachariah's apprenticeship; the loss of this led to a lawsuit later.

intended for Lichfield', that is, for the Royal garrison there. Foley had a covenant with King Charles to cast bar-iron, iron ordnance, grenades, shot, pike-heads and nails. Later, the Knights, too, found army contracts most profitable. Indirectly and later, the glass-makers were to profit, too; the melting down of gold and silver plate and vessels to assuage what the King called 'the incurable disease of want of money' to pay the soldiers, left dining tables bare of any drinking vessels but of earthenware and called for glass to take what was to be henceforth its fittest place.

Though not a Stour valley industry in the sense that it depended on the Stour for power[1] as did the iron forges, and the various mills, the glass industry was sited in that valley of which the town of Stourbridge with its many inns and its weekly market, its busy trades in wool, skins, leather, flax and hemp, was the hub. There is really no basis at all for the suggestion that the early glass-makers in this district lived in a sort of cloistered seclusion out of touch with the rest of the country. Consider the family of the first Joshua Henzey: Ananias, making glass and farming land in Ireland but also building a glass-house in Brettell; John, not only 'of Woolwich' but also of Hawbush in Brettell, one of the chief tenants of the Kingswinford manor and marrying a woman of Alcester; Joshua the Second travelling to and fro between Brettell and London and merchant in partnership with Robert Foley, official ironmonger to the Navy Office and friend of Samuel Pepys. Joshua's son, Thomas, marries a well-to-do Oxford lady, his daughters in turn marry men from Derbyshire, Uttoxeter, Covent Garden and Abbots Bromley; another of the third generation is 'John Henzey, gent. of Bristol'. By that time Thomas Milward, when away from his Stourbridge office, could be found if needed by the Henzeys, whose solicitor he was, at the Black Lion in Water Lane in Fleet Street, London; at home, he records that he had been doing business here with 'Mr. Henzey of Ireland'.

If the transport of heavy materials was a difficult matter in these pre-turnpike days, personal communication with the outside world was easy enough for it to have become general and constant. Besides Joshua Henzey and John, Jeremiah Bague had London interests and the Foleys had warehouses there. With that natural outlet for the Stour valley, Bristol, intercourse was even easier;

---

[1] This was to come later: John Dovey of Brettell Lane, 'the first to use wrought iron mills for cutting glass' was doing this at Woollaston Mill on the Stour in 1772. (Advertisement for 'apprentice to a glass cutter', *Birmingham Gazette*, 22 June 1772.)

PLATE 36. Four Dennis pieces, *circa* 1880.

PLATE 37. 'Rock Crystal', late nineteenth century.

here again the Foleys had premises; the Perrotts had settled there, soon to be followed by Littles and Rogers from Amblecote and Bradleys from Kingswinford. Even the transport of such heavy commodities as coal and fireclay had been made practicable as early as the sixteen-sixties by the prodigiously active and ingenious Andrew Yarranton; he had been associated with 'certain persons of honour' in a scheme to make the Stour navigable from Stourbridge to the Severn;[1] though 'they let it fall again' after obtaining the enabling Act of Parliament, Yarranton persisted with the project: 'it being a brat of my own I was not willing it should be abortive . . . I fell on and made it completely navigable from Stourbridge to Kidderminster and carried down many hundred tons of coal.' Over a hundred years later some of the boats Yarranton used were found; so reported Gough when editing the 1789 edition of Camden's *Britannia*. Gough found all the reasons generally given for Yarranton's abandonment of the final stages of the project unsatisfactory. 'We must therefore conclude', he wrote, 'that the numerous works and glasshouses upon the Stour and in the neighbourhood of Stourbridge did not then exist. A.D. 1666.' We find Gough's reasons even more unsatisfactory, for we know that many of these works and glass-houses were enjoying a vigorous existence in that year.

The early and easy absorption of the foreign glass-makers, Lorrainers and others, into local society is illustrated by the record of their civic activities. The Church was then the centre of civic as well as religious life and the parish was administered from the Vestry by the ratepayers assembled there, according to the Parish Book, the 'principal inhabitants'. The parish church was in the hamlet of Oldswinford, and there was the Vestry, a stubborn fact that for hundreds of years sorely irked Stourbridge townsmen, for this meant that, although there was in the very centre of the town a convenient public hall, the Town Hall, they had perforce to travel a mile or more to the sleepy southern extremity of the parish to be able to take any effective part in the government of the district; this meant chiefly deciding the amount of the rates they had to pay. The Manorial Courts, too, in the old lord's time had been held at the Gate-house, also in Oldswinford, but the

---

[1] Another similar scheme was in the air in 1676:
'. . . a Bill now before the lords for making a brook in Worcestershire navigable betwixt the Severn and Stirbridge that the coals there may be brought cheaper to Worcester Gloucester & these lower countreys which will absolutely destroy all the water sale of coals out of Shropshire. . . .'
from a letter of 17 May 1676

disgruntled and importunate townsmen had prevailed on the new lord, Sir John Lyttelton, to transfer the Courts Baron and Leet to the Town Hall.[1] But Stourbridge being no parish[2] had no Vestry and Oldswinford it had to be; through the years town and parish quarrelled about it, but town had always to toe the parochial line.

From the ratepayers assembled then in the Oldswinford Vestry the parish officials were chosen: Church Wardens, Overseers, Collectors, Supervisors of the Highways. As early as 1634, a Frenchman was chosen Church Warden, Mr. Jeremiah Bague; the 'Mr.' then was a significant tribute to a man's standing and not a courtesy title. In 1638, Joshua Henzey was an Overseer; the parish clerk's mind shied at spelling these outlandish names; when Joshua was appointed the clerk wrote him down as 'Joseph Hensex' but by the end of the year when he presented the account of his stewardship of public money he had become 'Josias Hensey'. In the next year 'Daniel Tyterr' filled the office. In 1643, 'Joshua Hensey' was Church Warden and was re-elected in the following year. The year 1655 brought overseer's office to Abraham Visitalia ('Wistolia' to the clerk), 1656 to James Durocher who by 1663 had become 'Durrossey'. The names of Caesar Racketts (Rachetti), Paul Henzey, Thomas Henzey, Zachary Tyzacke, Edward Henzey carry on the story of the active and responsible share these immigrants took in the communal life of their adopted home.

In the early sixteen-fifties John Henzey, 'John of Woolwich', bought the customary tenement later to be called Hawbush in the Kingswinford manor. The tenure of these 'customary' estates carried with it the duty of serving in turn the three chief lay manorial offices of Beadle, Reeve and Forester, each for one year. The Beadle's duties were the arrangements for the meetings of the manorial courts, the great Court, the Court Baron, which met every six months and the little Court, the Court Leet, which held regular sessions through the year every three weeks. The Reeve was in responsible charge of the agricultural programme for the great common fields of the manor. It was the Forester's duty to 'drive Pensnet and Ashwood foure times apeece within the years at the leaste according to the custome of the manner in pane for

---

[1] The lack of a Town Hall in Kingswinford meant that a much more convenient method of holding the Courts was used there, the sizable houses in the manor housing them in turn, Ashwood Lodge, Winsor James's house at Wordsley, the Brettells' house in Brettell, &c.

[2] There was no parish in Stourbridge town until 1866 when one was assigned to St. Thomas's Church.

not doeing the same to forfeite to the lord of the manner thirty nine shillings and aleaven pence.' This meant rounding up all the cattle grazing on these two commons, determining their ownership and ensuring that no tenant was exceeding his allowed quota. For the honour of this office the Forester had to pay the lord of the manor forty shillings. When a customary tenant died his heir, before receiving his lands, had by custom to pay one year's chief rent and also a 'Heriot'; by the custom of the Kingswinford manor this comprised gifts to the lord of the dead man's best beast, half his swine and half his bees; usually these gifts were commuted into a money payment.

John Henzey's name appears for the first time in the 1653 list of Customary Tenants written in the Court Rolls of the manor: it is one of twenty-nine; he had become an English gentleman.

Gradually the foreign names disappeared. Childless sons and fecund daughters marrying Englishmen meant that 'Henzey'[1] was replaced by Lloyd, Grove, Parnell, Rainsford, Brettell, Homfray, Dixon, Williams, Godwin, Bate and Pidcock; 'Tyzack' gave way to Hill, Lindon, Phillips, York, Rawlings, Baker, Hawkes; 'Tittery'[2] became Rogers and Bradley, and 'Bague' lost its identity in Hodgetts and Nash. The later history of the district is eloquent of the fact that, though these old names disappeared, the social status and substance achieved by those who had proudly borne them remained secure under the new ones.

[1] The name appears later as a Christian name:
John Henzey Dixon, b. 1770.
John Henzey Bate.
John Henzey Pidcock.
Henzey Pidcock, daughter of the first John Pidcock.
William Henzey Bond appears in an 1851 Directory.
[2] Daniel Tittery died in December 1641. The Titterys appear occasionally under the alias of 'Roja'.
In 1620 a 'David Tyttere, alias 'Rusher' was buried at Newcastle.
In 1687 a 'John Roja' was married at Broome (between 1676 and 1680 a Bague, a Durocher, a Squire and a Henzey were married there).

Chapter 7

MISSIONARIES AND VISITORS

In the sixteenth century it was written that

> 'Tous les Rois et Princes desiraient et affectaient avoir en leur royaulme cette science'

of glass-making; this was true not only of kings and princes but of monopolists and speculators, who bribed foreign masters of the craft to leave their native lands for strange furnaces and introduce that craft to other lands. Probably no craft so much as glass-making has been spread through the world by such devious traffic. The coveted immigrants were paid in advance, naturalized without delay or formality, excused taxes, and they most often repaid their generous if covetous hosts by refusing to teach their art, almost invariably blaming the stupidity of the native pupil. In Ireland, 'the foreign artists refuse to work with the Irish'; in Paris, 'Les ouvriers venitiens ne veulent rien enseigner aux francais'; in Virginia, 'they complaine that the Sand will not run'; in England 'all our glasse makers cannot fashion him one glass though he stood by them to teach them nor could the potter make him one pot to content him.' Edward VI got his foreign artists from Murano via Antwerp; Sir Robert Mansell from Mantua; they were cosseted, well-paid, comfortably lodged; they were put in the Tower on bread and water, but that one usual obligation of their contracts, that they should teach their craft so that 'the art should be known and wrought hereafter by our natural subjects', they obstinately refused to fulfil. Most of them went home, back to their native furnaces; some took money from the Venetian ambassador for their passage home and used it to get to Scotland where the monopolists were ready to welcome them and be defrauded in their turn.

The Lorrainers came here to stay; that this was their intent from the first is suggested by the almost immediate Englishing of their names. In 1568 they came to Sussex as de Hennezel, de Thiétry, du Thisac; as early as the fifteen-eighties we find Hensie, Tetrye, Tysacke; they reached Stourbridge, Henzey, Tyttery, Tyzack. They set out to be English, in their lives, their work, their worship; in Sussex they had been licensed to use Wisborough Church at fixed times with one of their number ministering and serving in French, here they knelt at the altar rails at Oldswinford and Kingswinford shoulder to shoulder with their English neighbours.

By 1662 Christopher Merret could write: 'Our own workmen in this Art have within these twenty years last past much improved themselves (to their own great reputation and the credit of our nation) insomuch that few foreiners are now left amongst us.' The Lorrainers were still amongst us (so many of them that the industry could not employ all the gaffers available) but they were now merged into the English community; they were Stourbridge glass-makers, like the Rogers, the Bradleys, the Batchelors. As we have seen, some of these redundant master-workmen left the district, but not to make glass; however, it was not long before native Stourbridge glass-makers began to journey to other distant places to make Stourbridge glass in these new homes.

The Perrotts were the first of these, though what connection these country gentlefolk of Belbroughton, who in the sixteenth century held the manor of Wollaston within the parish of Oldswinford, had with glass-making before they went to Bristol, is not known. However, once settled in the great western port, one of the busiest in Europe, they became actively interested in it and, if some marketed glass rather than made it, two at least were working glass-makers, John and Humphrey; they had been 'bred up and followed the trade and mystery of a Glass Maker'. They first made the Stourbridge broad-glass; we have seen members of the family partners with Thomas Henzey in the 1703 Cartel agreement; later, they turned with the prevailing fashion to crown-glass. By 1733, Humphrey was bankrupt; if he was not businessman enough to seize the opportunity the growing demand for crown-glass offered he was technically alive to the problems of his craft. What is more likely than that Humphrey, the 'ingenious gentleman', should have neglected the business side of his venture in his preoccupation with its technical problems? The new lead-glass metal was making particularly heavy demands on the resistant qualities of the pots: the intrusive action of the lead was destroying pot after pot of the traditional type. Humphrey busied himself on the problem of a new pot for the new metal.[1] In 1734, the year after he was declared bankrupt, he was given a fourteen-

---

[1] Two hundred years later the 'Society of Glass Technology' was still discussing the problem.

year patent for 'A furnace to contain Double Bottom Potts'; 'artificial draughts' were to raise the temperature of the furnace to the required degree in a quicker time by the use of less fuel and they would also better 'flash' the glass at the 'Teazing Holes', the 'Glory-holes' of the modern glass-maker. The specifications also include a new method of holding the glass while 'Nealing in the Kiln'[1] on what he called 'Mathematical Racks', made of 'Iron Clay or Stone or anything else that will endure the Fire.' The Kiln of the period 'a large oven' where the glass was 'nealed by the heate of ye furnace', was part of the pot furnace but at a higher level than the pot arches, so that the taker-in had to climb steps to put the glass in; a necessity which inevitably caused many breakages. The tunnel lehr had not yet been introduced into English glass-houses although Merret had described the use of it seventy years previously:[2]

> 'Glasses are put into Iron pans and drawn by the Sarole man all along the Leer which is 5 or 6 yards long, that the Glasses may cool Gradatim, for when they are drawn to the end of the Leer they become cold.'

Ten years later, the *Bristol Oracle* advertised 'To be sold the dwelling-house glasshouses &c late of Humphrey Perrott a bankrupt'.

Some members of the Little family of Amblecote had also made their way down the Severn valley to Bristol. The Hearth Tax returns for 1666 give the names of William and Jacob Little as householders in the 'Constablewick of Amblecoate'; in 1691, John Little of 'Stourbridge', glass-maker, was at work in Bristol and was apprenticing one of his sons to John Perrott, glass-maker; in 1703, Jacob Little was one of the witnesses to the Perrott-Henzey agreement. It was a Little who founded the famous Bedminster glass-house at which that most famous but most fragile opaque white glassware, which, especially with the painted decorations of Michael Edkins, was almost indistinguishable from delicate porcelain; at its best this glass, Thorpe claims, was 'never equalled in any country.' Another member of the family remained to make glass in Amblecote and while his Bristol kinsmen perfected their unique contribution to English glass, he was, according to Langford's 1760 list, producing 'flint glass, best and ordinary'.

[1] Celia Fiennes travelling through Castleton Bridge, Derbyshire, in 1697: 'saw them blowing White Glass and neale it in a large oven by the heate of ye ffurnace'.

[2] About 1780 George Ensell was using one of his own design at Coalbournbrook.

There was a Kingswinford Bradley too, who chose to settle and practise his craft in the western port; he it was who probably worked the Temple Backs glass-house which, then in the occupation of Robert Bradley & Company, was offered on lease in 1750. When 'Bradley's Tenement' at Wordsley, one of the customary tenancies of the Kingswinford manor, was made over to Robert Honeyborne in 1773, John Edwards 'of the city of Bristoll, Glassmaker' came as attorney for the Bradleys; the execution of such an office implies that Edwards was closely connected (maybe a Bradley's daughter's son) with the family.

John Henzey, grandson of the Ananias who had been the first Stourbridge glass-maker to settle in Ireland, his son, Bigoe Henzey, gent. and Jeremiah Rogers, one of the family working the Holloway End glass-house, all either made glass or traded it in Bristol.

When the Prince and Princess of Wales visited Bristol on 10 November 1738, they were entertained by a magnificent procession of the craft 'Companies of the City . . . in their formalities'. Pride of leading place in that gay parade was given to the 'Company of Glassmen' who must have been very busily 'friggering' in anticipation of the royal occasion for, riding on horseback in their 'white Holland shirts, some carried swords, others crowns and sceptres' all made of glass. In that leading group there must have been many members of Stourbridge glass-making families as there must have been, too, among Mr. Daniel Foley's 'well-selected workmen of superior skill' at Cork in the early years of the nineteenth century, who boasted 'a kind of music with glass instruments, bassoons, serpents, horns and trumpets' which so much impressed the Officer Commanding Cork District that he ordered a large glass trumpet 'the sound of which will reach to the shores of Seringapatam.'

In the sixteen-seventies two of the Altarist family of glass-makers, the Dagnias, spent some time in this district, Onesiphorus and Jeremiah. They probably came from Bristol where their father Edward was at work. There Edward met Dud Dudley. The company holding the monopoly of the new process of smelting of iron with pit-coal at the time had set up their furnaces in the Forest of Dean after a first failure at Bristol. They were meeting with no success, the pots in which they were smelting their ores constantly cracking under the fierce heat; knowing the glass-makers' cunning in making pots for their own use they called in to their aid 'an Ingenious Glass-Maker, Master Edward Dagney, an Italian then living in Bristow'. They also invited Dud Dudley to visit the new site, hoping that they would find him willing to give them the fruits of his long experience of the process.[1]

It may have been this association of Dud with Edward Dagnia that led to the coming of his sons into the Stourbridge district. They did not settle here as the Lorrainers had done but after some years went on to Newcastle upon Tyne, where Onesiphorus in 1684 founded a glass-house 'for making white glass and bottles';[2] this seems to have been the first introduction of the new glass of lead into the great northern centre where the staple product hitherto had been the broad-glass of the Lorrainers. In 1701 the Dagnias set up a second house in collaboration with a John Harrop. Nine years later both houses came into the possession of a John Williams, an ironworker who had turned to glass-making and had married the widow of the Dagnia last in possession. Of these two English partners of the Dagnias, Harrop may have gone from this district with the Dagnias; Harrops have made or cut glass here for many generations.[3] Williams, who followed later, was certainly an emigrant from Stourbridge.

Ireland had from the sixteenth century been a varyingly happy hunting-ground for English glass-makers. In 1589, George Longe, who had bought the Irish glass Monopoly from a Captain Wode-house, was proposing to Queen Elizabeth's minister, Burghley, that the number of glass-houses in England should be reduced from fifteen to four and work found for the displaced workmen in that island; he had, he comprehensively claimed, perfected glass-making in the two years he had spent there. We have already seen Abraham Bigoe and Henzeys settling and thriving there and Davy the Frenchman working a house for the Earl of Cork and we have noted Sir George Rawdon's 1665 invitation to Stour-bridge glass-makers to come and exploit the potentialities of the country. Crown window-glass as well as broad, flint-glass and bottles were being made in quantity from metal melted in pots of Stourbridge clay long before the famous Waterford and Cork glass was first produced.

In 1768, the Irish Parliament was being told of two Londoners

[1] Dud's father had held the monopoly from 1620 for fourteen years; Dud himself was granted the patent in 1638.

[2] Like Thomas Batchelor at Dennis, Onesiphorus fell foul of the exciseman: in 1697 he was fined £200 and costs for having fraudulently concealed over 2679 dozens of glass bottles.

[3] A Wordsley Harrop was working a glass-house at Bromsgrove from 1867: his son and sons-in-law until 1925.

PLATE 38. 'Rock Crystal' liqueur and claret jug, late nineteenth century.

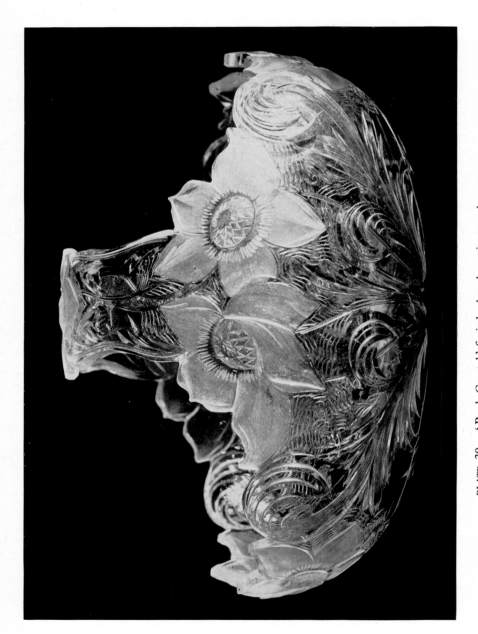

PLATE 39.   'Rock Crystal' fruit basket, late nineteenth century.

who had brought 'skilled artists from abroad to make flint glass'; in 1783, to support their plea for aid in establishing glass manufacture in Cork, the promoters stated that they had sent a 'proper person' to spy out the glass districts of England 'to take plans of all the most complete and extensive works, to procure experienced hands and the best materials.' The spies returned from this glass Goshen not only with 'the most ample set of materials and implements' but also 'with a set of the most able artificers England could afford.'

Two years later, in 1785, evidence was presented to a Committee of Inquiry into commercial relations between Great Britain and Ireland that three of every four glass-makers in Ireland were English immigrants and that English glass-makers were constantly going backwards and forwards to Ireland. Of these immigrants by far the most important was an Amblecote glass-maker, John Hill. 'Mr. Hill, a great manufacturer of Stourbridge,' the committee was informed, 'had lately gone to Waterford and had taken the best set of workmen he could get in the county of Worcester.'

The Hills had by this time become important figures in the industry; they had first become connected with it when Elizabeth Hill married Humphrey Batchelor of the Dennis Glass-house. Elizabeth was a daughter of the Hill family of the Tiled House tenement at Bromley, one of the customary tenancies of the Kingswinford manor. The Tiled House was well-known in the district as a long-established centre of the iron industry. At the end of the seventeenth century, John Haydon was making steel there by a secret cementation process; his iron and the carbonaceous material he used (his secret) were baked in sealed coffins made of the local fireclay in a round furnace, which he may have copied from glass-making practice; the process was original enough to merit the attention and mention of Doctor Plot, then professor of 'Chymistry' at the University of Oxford, in his *Natural History of Staffordshire*. The Hills had a blade-mill there and were scythesmiths; Waldron Hill (the 'Waldron' is token of another family connection of importance in the glass world) had married an Elizabeth Tyzack.

On Humphrey Batchelor's death, Elizabeth came into possession of Dennis. By 1777, when the property came into the hand of Thomas Hill, her nephew, the glass-house had 'fallen down and gone to decay'; but together with the ruins of the old Fimbrell house went a working glass-house at Coalbournbrook, next door to the Harlestones Henzey house.[1] Two years later, Thomas Hill bought this too for £200 from Oliver Dixon, grandson of John Henzey; it was then being worked by John Pidcock in partnership with George Ensell[2] and Richard Bradley; the works manager was Ensell, a noteworthy figure in Stourbridge glass history.

John Hill in 1776 was working a glass-house at Audnam[3] belonging to Thomas Raybould, another scythesmith, whose home was Amblecote Hall and whose works was the Lye Forge. It was probably from this glass-house that John Hill took most of the members of 'the best set of workmen he could get' to Waterford in the seventeen-eighties. There had been a glass-house at work there in 1711, making 'crown-glass and plate' and a second from 1729 producing 'all sorts of flint glass, double and single, also garden glasses, vials and other green glassware.' But it was to a new glass-house built by George and William Penrose in 1783 that Hill took over his chosen workmen. Like so many of the businessmen who dabbled in glass in Ireland as in England, the Penroses knew nothing of the trade, but with a capital of £10,000 they claimed to have 'established an extensive glass industry' which offered 'cut glass . . . useful as well as ornamental' and employed 'fifty to seventy men'; in their second year their claims took on this superlative air—they were turning out 'cut and

---

[1] For some time the Harlestones glass-house had been worked by Elijah Barrar, who made 'flint glass, best and ordinary' and 'phials' there. Elijah was the son of that Henry Barrar who had managed Dennis for Humphrey Batchelor for some years from 1728. Elijah failed and was declared bankrupt in 1767. The Barrars had some family connection with the Batchelors.

[2] The name 'Ensell' is often claimed to be a corruption of 'Henzey'. 'Ensell' however, appears in the Worcester Muster Rolls as early as 1539. The names appear together in the Kingswinford Parish Register and in the Court Rolls; in the latter, 'Jane Ensell, widow' in 1682.

George Ensell was at this time (1779) also in partnership with Robert Honeyborne at Moor Lane, and with Pidcock and Bradley at Wordsley.

D. N. Sandilands: 'Ensell a corrupted form of Henzey.'

S. E. Winbolt: 'A Hennezel, by this time Ensell. . . .'

W. A. Thorpe: '. . . Lorraine family Hennezel (Henzey Ensell). . . .'

[3] This was the glass-house sold by Edward Bradley in 1699 to John Wheeler, gent. of Wollaston Hall; Wheeler's heiress, Penelope, widow of Thomas Kynnersley, who had had glass interests, sold it in 1761 to John Pidcock, John Foxall and Thomas Raybould. In the early years of the nineteenth century Thomas Kinnersley, John Davenport and Edward Grafton were making and dealing in glass at Longport; their partnership was dissolved in 1807. Grafton, a Brettell Lane man, was works manager; in 1805 he had been advertising in the *Birmingham Gazette* for

'foot-blowers such as understand their trade, wages 12/- to 18/- a week'.

This John Davenport was probably the well-known potter.

engraved glass of as fine a quality as any in Europe'. John Hill became their manager and founder. In 1788 the firm sent 'a very curious service' of their glass, that is, of John Hill's glass, to the British Royal Family.

But by then, John Hill had already left the Penroses and Ireland. Personal relationships between him and one of the Penrose wives had reached a compromising pitch: accusations by the lady produced conditions which Hill could no longer tolerate. It was a sad predicament for a master craftsman, eager only for the task he had undertaken; 'My mind', he wrote at the time, 'is so hurt that I scarcely know what I am writing.' If Mistress Penrose had been willing to be too kind to her husband's employee, the Penrose clerk, Jonathan Gatchell, had been kind enough to the works manager to merit a farewell gift. As a token of his gratitude John Hill handed over to Gatchell his book of recipes, *Receipts for making Flint Enamel Blue and Best Green Glass*. The Waterford glass-house, under Hill's management and using his recipes, had, of course, been making Stourbridge glass; Gatchell, now in possession of its secrets, forced the Penroses to appoint him as their founder in Hill's place and by 1811, he was sole proprietor of the business.[1]

Many other men went from the Stourbridge district into the world, transferring their cunning and skill to other districts which they enriched with the fruits of their training here; men such as Benjamin Batchelor of Dennis who crossed the Severn into Shropshire and was making glass at Broseley in 1732. Others left with other varying motives: Doctor Pococke, visiting Prescot near Ormskirk on one of his *Travels through England*, in June 1751 found that

> 'They had a manufacture of green glass but the house has been taken by one of Sturbridge[2] in Worcestershire in order to shut it up.'

And in 1769 Samuel Richards of Wordsley, 'an apprentice to the glass-engraving business' was being sought by advertisement having 'absconded his masters' service'; Newcastle upon Tyne was his suspected destination. In 1767 Samuel Benedict, an 'Engraver of Glass', being bankrupt, went off first to London and

[1] The firm used Stourbridge fire-clay: Joshua Wright in 1834 visited this district 'where our day merchants reside, one of them being James Holland'.

[2] 'Sturbridge'; it is so in the Court Rolls; just as it is in the speech of the elders of the district today.

then to Manchester where he had a 'large quantity of all kinds of cut glass.'[1]

The district had its visitors, too; a few fortunately left some record of their visits behind. At the very beginning of the eighteenth century, that indefatigably curious traveller, Celia Fiennes, rode through and tells us how, making for Churchill near 'Sturbridge', she saw 'the many Glass Houses where they blow broad glass'. A more famous traveller, Daniel Defoe, a quarter of a century later, viewed the district from the dim distance of Worcester city. In the second volume of his *Tour through England and Wales*, published in 1725, he writes: 'There are three or four especial manufactures carried on in this country, which are peculiar to itself.' The second speciality he described as

'Fine stone potts for the glass-makers melting their metal, of which they make their fine flint glass, glass plates, &c. not to be found any where but at Stourbridge in this county, the same clay makes crucibles and other melting pots.'

At the end of his list he adds:

'At Stourbridge also they have a very great manufacture for glass of all sorts.'

It is regrettable that this competent journalist did not come near enough and stay long enough to be as informingly explicit about this 'very great manufacture' as he was, for instance, about the Yorkshire woollen industry.

In 1751, Doctor Richard Pococke (later to be successively Bishop of Meath and of Ossorry) travelled through the district. Riding down from Dudley across Pensnett Chase, not yet enclosed, 'most part of the way by coal works' and the 'many forges for working of iron in different ways' and wondering at the 'spirit of industry' which prevailed everywhere:

'We came to Sturbridge famous for its glass manufactures especially its coloured glass with which they make painted windows which is here coloured in the liquid of all the capital colours in their several shades, and, if I mistake not, is a secret which they have here.'[2]

[1] One of the best known of later missionaries was Fred Carder. Born at Wordsley in 1864 to a family of potters, he was at seventeen designing for Stevens & Williams. He remained with the Brierley Hill firm until 1903 when he went to the United States to become first manager of the later famous Steuben Glassworks. From 1918 to 1934, when he retired, he was 'Director of Art' at the Corning Glassworks, New York.

[2] W. A. Thorpe says that there is evidence that coloured glass was made in England before the end of the seventeenth century.

PLATE 40.   Low jug.   Silver Deposit Design, 1886.

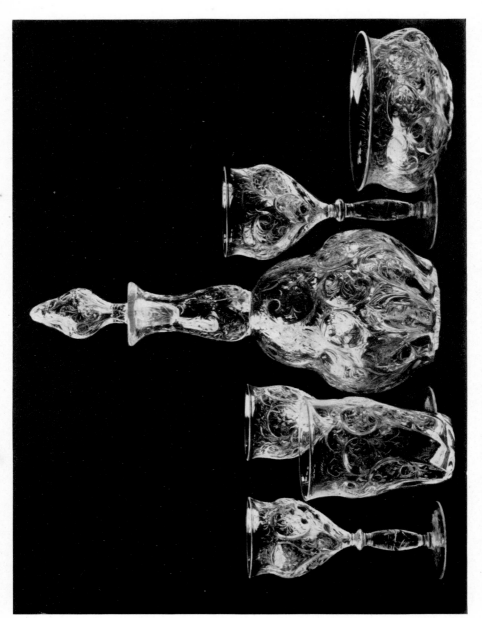

PLATE 41. 'Rock Crystal' Table Set, late nineteenth century.

Five years later, Dr. Pococke came again, approaching Stourbridge this time from the opposite direction and visiting Hagley
Church on the way; he described its east window of 'rich painted
glass made in 1569'; Flemish glass this, but bordered, as were
also the three windows on each side, with

> 'blue purple and green glass lately made at Stourbridge . . .
> coloured glass thrown into pretty Gothic figures.'[1]

An anonymous gentleman touring the district in 1776 and
writing LETTERS *on the Beauties of* HAGLEY ENVIL *and
the* LEASOWES was on his way between the first two of these
beauty spots when

> 'Seeing Stourbridge before me, a town eminent for its glass
> manufactory I was induced having never seen the curious art
> of forming that delicate ware into its various uses, to break-
> fast there and satisfy my curiosity. . . . I was really aston-
> ished to see with what facility a process was conducted, that
> always appeared to me so extremely mysterious—but com-
> monly the most impenetrably one seemingly, when known
> appears so very simple, that we are equally astonished the
> other way, and blush at our ignorance in not being able to
> find it out without a demonstration; so in the art of glass-
> making, particularly the introducing of those beautiful spiral
> threads of a different colour, so nicely spun within the neck
> of a wine glass, which appear so inexplicable, is performed,
> even by children. One of these glasses I desired to be made
> me as elegant as possible which was done almost as soon as
> asked for.'

The ease with which this elegant specimen of 'that delicate ware'
had been made seems to have given him a false value of its worth
and substance. He put it in his pocket with the inevitable result:

> 'I put the glass into my pocket, which the half-burnt,
> cadaverous looking animal made me, wishing to preserve it;
> but the first stile I came to, demolished it for ever.'

[1] Dr. Pococke had also travelled widely and observantly on the Continent:
in 1736, twenty years before this Hagley visit, he was writing about German
cut-glass—large drinking glasses 'so finely cut as to sell for from 100 li to
150 li', the glass being 'the best in the world'. Bohemian glass was 'thick and
strong and almost as good as the English'.

Chapter 8

THE EXCISE PERIOD

There was money in glass in the eighteenth century. In the first half of the century we find 'Thomas Rogers of the Hill,[1] Amblecote, glass manufacturer' and in the next generation 'Thomas Rogers late of the Hill, Amblecote, now of Newington, Middlesex, banker'. At Coalbournbrook, Hill and Waldron are 'glassmakers' in 1771 and in 1789 'bankers and glass manufacturers'. Or the banker turned to glass for security: '1793 Rufford & Co. bankers' and in 1801 'Francis Rufford & Sons glassmakers'. Thomas Hill retired from Coalbournbrook to Monmouthshire and by his will left four daughters £6000 each, an annuity of £110 to 'my friend Miss Eliza Cook' and one of £100 to Sarah Brazier. Bachelor Richard Bradley of Wordsley spread his munificence over a wider field; his brothers, sisters, nephews and nieces, his ground bailiff, his engineer, his manager, his friends were all remembered and rewarded: £500 each to four nieces, a year's wages to all his household servants, £10 each to his apprentices, a week's wages to every person 'employed in and about my Glasshouse'.

When a 'meeting of Noblemen, Magistrates, Gentlemen, Farmers, Millers & others' at the Talbot Inn decided to raise a 'Subscription to defray the extra Expenses of Procuring CORN and other kinds of provisions' at a time of exorbitant prices, only the noble landowners with their hundred or fifty guineas gave more liberally than the glass-makers, the Pidcocks, the Honeybornes, with their tens and fives. Towards the establishment of an 'Association for the protection of Persons and Properties' again the glass-makers, two Pidcocks, two Honeybornes and a Wheeley with their twenty guineas each, subscribed most generously of the non-noble patrons. If Lord Dudley and Ward could take up ten of the three hundred shares[2] (the maximum allotment) in the new Stourbridge Navigation Company, so could 'Robert Honeyborne of Moor Lane, Glassmaker', and follow

[1] 'The Hill' is the older part of the present-day Corbett Hospital.
[2] These shares were selling at £350 each in 1793, £280 in 1851.

this with three (Thomas Honeyborne with three more) in the Dudley Navigation while Michael Grazebrook held two and a half.[1]

Such obvious prosperity invited predatory attention in those comparatively lawless days; in the July of 1771, the *London Gazette* reported:

'Thomas Willetts, clerk or agent to Waldron Hill and Thomas Hill of Amblecoat, glassmakers, was robbed of £125.2.6 money of the said Waldron Hill and Thomas Hill and also of William Waldron of Stourbridge glassmaker and a partner with the said W. Hill and T. Hill.'

In November 1777 Thomas Millward, the attorney, seeking to raise a loan, received the following answer from William Waldron:[2]

'I wish I could assist you with the sum you require. Give me leave truly to assure you my inclination is not wanting but you must believe me when I tell you it is out of my power to raise you any sum at present unless I shut up the Glasshouse. Since the additional Duty our payments there are enormous a sum not less than 600 li for duty every seven weeks.'

It was not only the common thief and the not uncommon borrower who had been attracted by the prosperity of the industry; another interested observer was an institution that needed neither to thieve nor borrow but could lawfully take—the Treasury.

The 'additional Duty' mentioned by Waldron had just been imposed; it was an addition to that which the Government had laid on the industry in 1745; still further additions were to be made in 1781 and 1787 and, despite general and continuous protests from the industry, these duties were for a hundred years to hinder its development, to stifle improvements, to harass manufacturer and maker and to encourage fraud; so, at least, the glass manufacturers claimed.

As we have seen, this was not the industry's first experience of fiscal exactions; Parliament during Cromwell's Protectorate, copying Dutch practice, had passed an ordinance which decreed a payment of

---

[1] In the Palfrey Collection is a statement of expenses of a journey in 1774 on horseback from London to Stourbridge via High Wycombe, Oxford, Stratford and Birmingham, which gives some idea of the money values of the time.

The journey began on the morning of 13 August and ended on 16 August; the only expense on the last day was 'Turnpikes, 2*d*.'. Food for man and mare for three full days, three nights' lodging and stabling, tips (boots, ostlers, waiters and chamber-maids 4*s*. 4*d*., and turnpikes 1*s*. 6½*d*.) cost in all £1 3*s*. 8½*d*.

[2] This letter is in the Palfrey Collection.

'12d. on every 20s. value of Glass of all sorts made in the
Kingdom to be paid by the Maker.'

We have noted the successful campaign which the country's
glass-makers carried out against the 'War Tax on Glass &
Earthen Wares' imposed in 1695 so that this was taken off in
1699. There was to be no such happy and early outcome to the
new campaign of protest. It was not until 5 April 1845, after a
full century of experience of running an industry 'under the
arbitrary control of a class of men to whose will and caprice it is
most irksome to have to submit & under regulations most un-
graciously inquisitorial' that the Richardsons of Wordsley could
write to their customers:

'We herewith hand you new List of Prices commencing this
day on the abolition of the duty on Glass.'

A significant sentence follows:

'It may perhaps be necessary to remove many erroneous
impressions which prevail to state the late duties upon Glass
removed by the government viz. on Window and German
Sheet Glass 8½d per lb, on Plate Glass 6½d per lb—on Flint
Glass and Black Bottles, three farthings per lb so that the
reduction of duty cannot influence the price of Flint and Cut
Glass to any extent.'

Actually Richardsons reduced their prices for 'the leading articles
of the trade' by 1d. per lb.

Throughout the period, even when the duties had been much
heavier than those quoted, the chief objection of the industry had
been to the method of collection rather than to the rates at which
the duties were levied; manufacturers were perfectly willing to pay
duties (though at lower rates) so long as they were protected
against the competition of imported glass by a tax on this. But

'We cannot do one single act in the conduct of our own business without having previously notified our intention to the
officers. We have in the course of a week's operations to
serve 60 or 70 notices on these our masters'

one glass-maker told the Commissioners of Excise; and another:

'These notices are so numerous that I have them printed by
the thousand; we have to give notices all day long.'

'It is astonishing', said a third,

'how Flint Glass works exist at all under such a concentration of commercial and manufacturing hindrances as are
imposed by the Excise regulations.'

The amount of duty payable was calculated on the weight of

PLATE 42. 'Rock Crystal' decanters,
late nineteenth century.

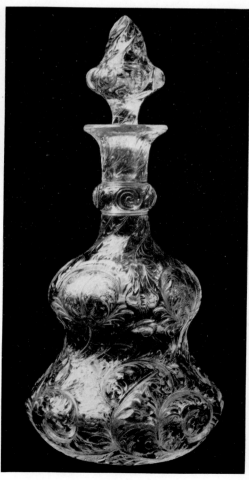

Great Exhibition of the Works of Industry of all Nations, 1851.

PRESIDENT,

HIS ROYAL HIGHNESS PRINCE ALBERT, K.G.

&c. &c. &c.

OFFICE FOR THE EXECUTIVE COMMITTEE,

Exhibition Building,

Kensington Road, London.

7 July, 1851.

Gentlemen

I am commanded by Her Majesty the Queen to desire that you will send a similar glass to that Numbered 301½ in your Stall with a venetian foot to Buckingham Palace and at the same time forward the account to Col. The Hon C B Phipps

I am.
Yr obbSert

Henry Cole

Mess Richardsons

By courtesy of the Librarian, Brierley Hill Library Collection.

PLATE 43   Royal Order to Richardsons, 1851.

materials used; a percentage of this was allowed for the inevitable loss sustained at different stages of the glass-making process and by accident. The net weight was checked at the delivery end of the lehr. Since the manufacturer was not trusted to supply the details of any of these weighings the Excise officer had to be present, in person or by deputy, from the first stage to the last; to check the amount of batch put into the pot, to weigh the finished glassware taken from the lehr and to ensure that there was no tampering with pot or lehr between these two weighings. If the regulations had allowed the Excise officer to assess the amount of duty on the weight of the glassware produced, there would have been many fewer objections to his constant and irksome presence. Regular visits to the sorting room would then have been all that was necessary; the officer would have been no more unwelcome, if more frequent, a visitor than those other collectors, the Overseers of the Poor or the Supervisors of the Highways.

It was the Excise officer's official preoccupation with the pot and its contents that manufacturers and glass-makers found so vexatious. First, no pot could be moved from the drying to the annealing arch except in his presence; then the pot had to be 'gauged', that is, its internal dimensions had to be measured under his prying eye and registered by his restless pencil; next the pot could not be set in the furnace or filled without his attention; nor could the metal be ladled out for testing in his absence. For each of these items it was a statutory requirement that the officer should be given six hours' written notice of the intention to perform it.

Once the pot was filled and in the furnace constant surveillance was carried on to ensure that nothing was added to its contents; the throwing into the pot of the smallest piece of cullet, for instance, or any other ingredient of the batch incurred, if detected, a penalty of £50. There were three officers to every glass-house; this guaranteed unbroken supervision, the three working in shifts so that one was on the spot at all hours of the day and night.

Especially intimate precautions were taken with the lehr; first it had to be

'rectangular in form, with only one entrance and with a sufficient iron grating affixed thereto, together with proper locks and other fastenings for securing the same'.

The 'proper locks' were specially provided by the officer at the manufacturer's expense; the keys were in the custody of the officer.

Here again written notice had to be given of every item in the lehr programme; having received this for the final weighing, the officer checked the number of pans emptied; the ware was then placed again under lock and key, the key handed into the keeping of the officer until the notice given to the supervisor had expired when he came to weigh it.

The pans were drawn through the lehr by an endless chain; the efficiency of a chain is the efficiency of its weakest link and links were always breaking and they broke when their breaking-point was reached irrespective of whether the official holding the keys of the lehr was on duty or not. If such an accident happened when this officer was off duty, let a manufacturer tell what happened:

> 'either the whole works must be stopped or some mode adopted for the lear man to repair the mischief not strictly in keeping with the Act; so that while the owner is quietly reposing in his bed in imaginary security his servant unknown to him has almost necessarily incurred ruinous Excise penalties.'

Actually three payments had to be made by the manufacturers; first, an annual licence which 'licensed and empowered A.B. to exercise or carry on the Trade or Business of a Glassmaker at X'; second, a payment on every pound of batch melted, which was calculated from the 'gauging' of the pots—the internal dimensions and the surface level of the metal in them, this level being measured by an iron 'gauging-rod to measure the depth of the vacuity above the surface of the metal'; the third payment was one on every pound in weight of goods produced above forty per cent of the weight of the batch from which they were made; this percentage was eventually raised to fifty.

There has always been, and inevitably, a good deal of waste of metal in glassmaking, the amount varying with the type of product. Where the wine-glass workman during the Excise period, used no more than a third of the metal he gathered, the phial maker used more than two-thirds; much of this waste was used as cullet in the next batch. There were accidental breakages, there was irrecoverable loss from faulty pots. The manufacturers claimed throughout the period that the regulation allowance for this waste, which had to be accounted for every week, was entirely inadequate. The more waste there was, the less the weight of goods delivered under the officer's eyes at the end of the lehr and the greater the possibility of this falling below the required forty per cent.

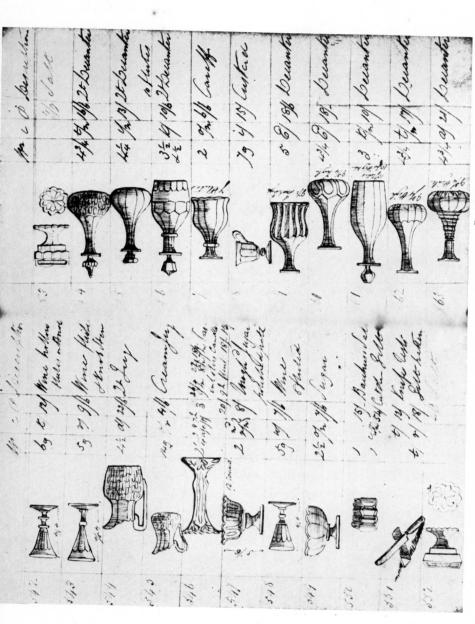

PLATE 44. Pages from the first Stevens & Williams MS. Price List.

PLATE 45. A vase with applied colour ornament.

Naturally enough, a good deal of evasion was practised and to much of this the Excise officers, recognizing that strict enforcement of some of the regulations would practically bring the industry to a standstill, turned blind eyes; they saw, said one manufacturer, that unless the industry practised what was 'questionable fraud' in self-defence, there would soon be neither living for the maker nor revenue for the government:

> 'the evil had long been productive of evasion and immorality without any security to the Revenue.'

This 'miserable' duty, said a member of the House of Commons in 1830 was 'a source of endless oppression and fraud'. The Excise Commissioners themselves admitted that 'evasion of the duty could not be prevented by any addition to the laws or regulations'.

The Excise regulations, comprehensive as they were, had occasionally to be more explicitly defined for puzzled manufacturers; it is not surprising to find the Commissioners exploiting such occasions to the benefit of the Exchequer and quite in character for them to spend months on finding how to do this. In June 1842, Ben Richardson of Wordsley, deciding that some 'flower glasses' he had (probably first intended to be held in a metal stand) would be improved by the addition of 'fresh legs or pillars' and proposing to do this by 'heating them and sticking fresh metal thereto and depositing the same in the Lears to be again annealed' enquired of the Commissioners about the amount of duty he would have to pay since duty had already been paid on the legless glasses. It took the Commissioners three months to make what was obviously to them a very easy decision that

> 'the Flower Glasses remaining perfect when taken from the Lears be weighed and charged with Duty as well in the first instance as when subsequently drawn from the Lears.'

Payments of the duty were made every 'round' of six or seven weeks; in the earliest days of the period, in 1749, we have seen Thomas Batchelor at Dennis paying £249 12s. 2d. and William Waldron in 1777 claiming that he was paying £600 every round. Halfway through the period in 1793 the *Universal British Directory* reported that the ten glass-houses in the Stourbridge district were paying £20,000 a year; in the second half of 1838, seven years before the duty was taken off, Richardsons of Wordsley paid a total of £1,258 6s. 6d.

In spite of the duties, the industry, as we have seen, prospered; there is no evidence that Serjeant Witton's bankruptcy at the Heath in 1801 was in any way due to them. Manufacturers made sizable fortunes; they set up country banks, they built fine houses, they bought land, they invested in other industries. Macpherson's *Annals of Commerce* reported in 1783 (after the trade had for nearly forty years 'groaned under a system of excise exaction and supervision to the injury of the trade as a trade . . . a concentration of commercial and manufacturing hindrances') that the value of the annual produce of the English glass trade was £630,000 and was 'rapidly increasing'. As at least one of every four glasshouses in the country was in the Stourbridge district, about £160,000 worth of glass must have been produced here. Obviously the 'commercial hindrances' were being fairly easily overcome; what of the 'manufacturing hindrances'?

'The surveillance of pots', one maker claimed, 'was almost a prohibition of alteration of tint or experiments and consequent improvements'; the Excise Commissioners agreed that 'the regulations are a great impediment and in many cases a complete bar in the way of experimental researches.'

It was the flint-glass manufacturer who was most seriously affected, for it was his pots, not those of the makers of plate-glass or bottle-glass, that were so closely watched by the unlidded eye of officialdom. Now seven or eight of the ten glass-houses at work here made more than one kind of glass: flint-glass and bottles, flint-glass and plate, flint and phials; that is, some of their pots were free of supervision. Could not the necessary 'experimental researches' have been made in these? If the glass-makers had not thought of such an expedient, the regulation-makers certainly had and had forestalled it. No such 'overlapping' was allowed; in a flint-glass house only flint-glass could be made; no flint-glass could be made in a window-glass house, no bottle-glass in a plate-glass house and so on, every different kind cribbed, cabined and confined in a sealed seclusion.

Yet there must have been some experiment; the famous 'Bristol' opaque white glass, for instance, was developed to its final perfection during the period. If there was little chance for research with a view to improving the quality of the metal, there was no hindrance to experiment in the decoration of vessels made from that metal. Since the amount of duty was calculated on the weight of the glass, it was obviously good business to increase the sales-value of each piece of glass in every possible way, by engraving, by cutting. Whatever aesthetic motives influenced the development of decorative glass-cutting, there is little doubt that the commercial, the profit, motive was originally stronger.

Whatever the annoyances caused by official supervision, the actual payment of the duty caused no greater hardship to the manufacturers here than, perhaps, a temporary shortage of ready cash at the end of each round; they recovered their payments in their prices and, as we have seen, they continued to prosper. When a Turnpike Trust was set up by Act of Parliament to take over the Stourbridge–Wolverhampton road as far as Wordsley, the Commissioners appointed were required to swear on oath that they were

> 'in receipt of the rents and profits of lands . . . of the clear yearly value of fifty pounds . . . or intitled to real and personal estate together to the value of one thousand pounds'.

In the list of Commissioners appears the name of every glass manufacturer in the district.

What was the need for this Trust? A traveller in 1771 wrote:

> 'Staffordshire roads are wonderful to strangers. When they are mending, as they call it, you travel over a bed of stones none of them of less size than an octavo volume and where not amended it is like a stair case.'

Until they were turnpiked, midland roads were no more than traditional tracks; they were unmade and received only such haphazard attention as an unpaid Supervisor of the Highways, appointed yearly by the Vestry, could prevail on unwilling parishioners (though they were statutorily required to do six days' work a year on the roads of the parish) to give.

> 'The rich do so cancel their portions and the poor so loiter that of the six scarcely two good days work are performed . . . each Surveyor amendeth such lanes as seem best for his own commodity and more easy passage into his fields and pastures.'

The heavy industrial traffic in this district, the carriage of the coal which was being raised in rapidly increasing quantities from the pits on Pensnett Chase to the forges and mills of the Stour valley, had 'daily worn out the Highways with Waggons carrying excessive Burdens'. The heavily-loaded broad-wheeled waggons had been introduced to cope with the growing demand for coal which the old packhorse-trains had been unable to satisfy. As early as 1699, these trains were carrying coal at 5½d. a horse-load (5 to 6 cwt.) to Cradley Forge, at 12d. a load to Cookley Slitting Mills and at 14d. to Wilden Forge and Mill and we have noted Andrew Yarranton's temporarily successful attempt before that date to carry the coals by the Stour itself from Stourbridge to

Kidderminster.[1] The waggons failed, they soon made the roads impassable and in dry weather their broad wheels ground the surface into deserts of dust, in wet weather they became bogged in sloughs, their draught horses and oxen floundering knee-deep in the mud; the pack animals were brought back, horse, ass, mule, with their pairs of panniers balanced over their backs.[2]

It was along such roads and by such means that the glass manufacturers had to fetch in their raw materials and send out their wares. In the industry's earliest days, the sheets and quarries of broad-glass had been carried to its customers by an even older beast of burden than horse or ass, by man himself. The glass hawker, 'qui portat vitra ad dorsum', had borne his brittle burden abroad, packed in a shallow wooden crate slung on his back; though the pedlars and hawkers of other commodities had been suppressed as rogues and vagabonds, so respectable an aura did their goods bestow on the itinerant glass-hawkers that they were made free of the road.

Not even this signal official favour, however, had been sufficient in 1636 to prevent one of them, a 'Crate-carrier', being assaulted in Stourbridge, an offence which brought a fine of two shillings and sixpence on his assailant from the Court Leet.[3] Later, glass shared the hazards of carriage by packhorse or waggon with the other products of local industry which were in demand, coal, iron and fireclay, along these hardly passable roads. All save one (the Heath) of the eighteenth-century glass-houses of Stourbridge district stood on or near one of three of these ancient tracks: the Stourbridge–Wolverhampton road, the road from the bottom of Brettell Lane which led over Brierley Hill and Pensnett Chase to Scotts Green where it joined up with the third, the Dudley–Kingswinford road.

The first of these roads left Stourbridge town by the narrow four-arched bridge[4] over the Stour, then climbed through the deep and narrow hollow-way[5] which the heavy traffic and the chan-

[1] Richard Baxter tells how in one hard winter Kidderminster men dug through the snow across the Heath in an attempt to get coal to the town; some actually perished in the attempt.

[2] Oldswinford Churchwarden Accounts: '1772. 4 Ass Load of Coals ... 0:03:0.'

[3] John Robinson, a 'Glass Carrier', was buried at Kingswinford in 1717.

[4] A halfpenny token struck in 1668 showed a bridge of four arches and the name John Pratt on the obverse and 'StourBridge 1668' and 'His Half Peny' on the reverse.

[5] 'Holloway End'—the glasshouse site used to be more often called 'Hollowsend'; it appears so in documents of the seventeenth century; fifty years ago Amblecote Church was always popularly called 'Hollowsend Church'.

PLATE 46.   Engraved and cut goblet, late
nineteenth century.

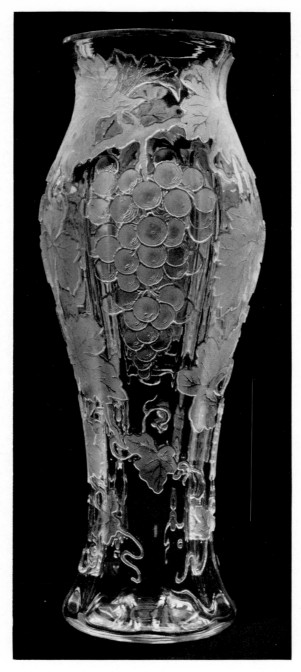

PLATE 47. 'Crystal Cameo' vase,
late nineteenth century.

nelled rains had cut through the sand; it forded the Coalbourn Brook (the Amblecote name for the Delph Brook) and after another half-mile forded a second, Audnam Brook; it climbed Camp Hill through another hollow-way then dropped down again to ford a third stream, Wordsley Brook; from this, it climbed on to the level stretch which brought it to Townsend (now the Cross, Kingswinford); the other two roads climbed from this road towards Dudley.

Two Turnpike Trusts[1] were empowered by Acts of Parliament to take over two of the three; one based on Stourbridge was responsible for the Wolverhampton road as far as Wordsley Green; the other for the Dudley–Kingswinford road and the Wolverhampton road from Townsend to 'the further End of Brittel Lane'.

The Commissioners appointed by Parliament were supposed to make and keep the roads serviceable and were allowed to levy tolls on all traffic using them to cover the cost of maintenance. The evidence in the minutes of the *Stourbridge Road Order Book*[2] is eloquent either of these gentlemen's preoccupation with other matters or of their very strong objection to the honour Parliament had thrust upon them. A common memorandum by the clerk reads: 'at which time and place there was not a Sufficient Number of Trustees present either to hold or adjourn the same.' However, by appointing paid surveyors and giving them a more or less free hand and by raising loans on the security of the tolls,[3] they greatly improved the Stourbridge–Wolverhampton road. They widened it from the town to Coalbournbrook, they replaced the narrow bridge by a wider one of one arch instead of four, they built culverts over the three streams which had hitherto been forded, and levelled the road over them, and they erected a weighing-machine at Coalbournbrook.[4] If the results of the glass-makers' efforts as Trustees did not fully merit Defoe's encomium that 'turnpikes are very great things and very great things are done by them', at least traffic to and from their glass-houses on this road could now move with more ease and in greater security.

A much more effective contribution to the solution of the district's traffic problem was to be made by a further Act of

---

[1] Stourbridge Road Acts: 1753 and 1772. Dudley-Kingswinford: 1726 and 1747.

[2] Palfrey Collection.

[3] Some from the 'Stourbridge Bank Coy'; but occasionally from glassmakers without interest; in 1786 Thomas Rogers, Thomas Hill, and 'Messrs. Pidcock & Grazebrook' lent the Trust £100 each.

[4] This building was demolished in 1952 in clearing the site for Piper Place.

Parliament in 1775, which empowered the 'Company of Proprietors . . . to make a Canal navigable and passable for Boats Barges and other Vessels' which was to begin 'in Amblecoat'[1] and to be continued 'to a Brook called Wordsley Brook and from thence to Stourton there to join with the Staffordshire and Worcestershire Canal'; it also gave the 'Authority of Parliament' for the making of 'Two collateral Cuts, one from . . . the Fens upon Pensnet-chace to communicate with the Canal near the junction of Wordsley-brook with the River Stour, and the other from . . . Black Delph . . . to The Lays there to join . . . the first collateral Cut.' The purpose of the project was 'to render the Carriage of Coal Ironstone and Limestone much easier and cheaper than at present.'

If the canal and its collaterals had been designed for the convenience of the glass-houses instead of the mines on Pensnett Chase, their route could not have been more happily planned; no glass-house in the district (save the Heath) was as much as a quarter-mile from some branch of the canal; some stood on its banks (Bague's, Wheeley's and Richard Bradley's), to others, such as Coalbournbrook and the Platts, basins brought materials directly into the works premises. 'The Company of Proprietors' of this 'Stourbridge Navigation' were authorized to raise a capital of £30,000 divided into three hundred 'equal shares' and 'no Person or Body Politic' was to have more than ten of these.[2] Among the original shareholders were the following glassmen: Edward Russell, John Pidcock, George Ensell, Thomas Hill, Thomas Raybould, William Scott, James Keir and Robert Honeyborne; of these the last took up the maximum allotment of ten shares.

The canal immediately brought relief to the overburdened roads; its waters were never still. By 1792, the Company's shares were selling at £350. In the first six months of 1798, 44,000 tons of coal and 'merchandise' were taken off the roads and borne in barges along its course, three-quarters of them coal and at a profit of £1,505 10s. 11¼d. to the Company. In 1801 a dividend of £14 7s. per share was being paid.[3]

The nineteenth century dawned on an England which, except

[1] The 'trench' here, a part of Yarranton's navigable Stour, was included in the canal basin.

[2] Permission was given by the amending Act of 1781 to increase this to £43,000.

[3] In the second half of 1824 the tonnage carried was 92,600 tons, a little less than half being coal.

PLATE 48.   The Dennis Chandelier awarded the Grand Prix at the Paris
Exhibition of 1878. Rearranged to carry ninety candlelights
it was awarded a second Grand Prix at the Paris Exhibition
of 1889.

PLATE 49.   A Dennis Chandelier.

for the hilly north, had been opened up by the inter-communicating canal systems. Black bottles were going by barge from Bristol to London and Lynn sand was coming to Brierley Hill; in the August of 1804 the canals brought Messrs Honeyborne and Batson of Moor Lane[1] twenty tons of it at thirty-two shillings the ton, while in the first six months of 1805, nine and a half tons of lead in barrels containing on an average nine hundredweights each, thirty-three barrels of ashes (about $5\frac{1}{4}$ tons) and twenty-five tons of sand[2] reached the firm from Liverpool by canal carriage.

[1] Forerunners of Stevens and Williams.
[2] Prices: Lead, 16s. 1d. per ton; Ashes, 30s. per ton and Sand at 13s. per ton as compared with Lynn sand at 32s.

Chapter 9

GEORGE ENSELL AND
THE WORDSLEY GLASS-HOUSES

At their meeting in the Adelphi on 22 January 1778, 'The Society for the Encouragement of Arts, Manufactures & Commerce', according to their minutes,

'Took into Consideration the single Claim for plates of Glass—Class 201.'

Seven sheets of glass of which 'three are broke' were examined and two certificates read by the five members present.[1] The first certificate was from a Richard Peterson, 'Officer of Excise', who testified that

'he has charged his Majesty's Duty of fourteen Shillings p. Cwt of Sheet Glass made by Mr. George Ensell of Amblecoat near Stourbridge';

the second was a report by 'John Beazeley Surveyor' that

'Mr. Ensell has in his Warehouses Fifty Sheets of Sheet Glass and that the Dimentions of each Sheet is not less than Thirty six Inches in length and twenty six Inches in Breadth'.

Accepting this testimony and satisfied by their own examination of the seven sheets, the meeting resolved

'that the Claimant having answered the purpose of the Society's Advertisement is entitled to fifty pounds being the Premium offered'.

In 1768, the 'Coalbournbrook Glasshouse' had been let by Oliver Dixon, grandson of John Henzey of Harlestones, to John Pidcock, George Ensell and Richard Bradley; two of these partners were already firmly established in the industry, John Pidcock (in all but name a Henzey) at the Dial and Platts houses and Richard Bradley making 'flint glass best and ordinary' at his Wordsley house; the third was new to ownership. The similarity of the name 'Ensell' to 'Hennezel' and the fact that he was a broad-glass maker have given rise not merely to suggestions that 'Ensell'

[1] These were Mr. John Wingfield, James and William Adam (architects), John Boydell (noted engraver) and Christopher Pinchbeck (son of the maker of the alloy).

might be a corrupt form of 'Hennezel' but to assured statements that it is so.[1]

The name 'Ensell' actually appears in a Worcester Muster Roll as early as 1539. It is incredible that in a district where the name of 'Henzey' (the English spelling used by the family now for over two hundred years) had for so long been an honoured name in the industry, a member of the family should use this spelling in preference. What is more, none of the biblical Christian names to which the Lorrainers were so attached, Joshua, Ananias, Zacharias, Elisha, Benjamin, appear among the Ensells; they are George, Edward, Joseph, John, Richard, Charles. 'Ensell' (often appearing as Ensall or Insall)[2] is more likely to be a variant of 'Insall'; 'John Insall, glassman' appears in the Kingswinford Parish Register in 1719.

The new man at Coalbournbrook signed the indenture of the lease 'George Ensell', and, corrupt or genuine, the name soon became of note in the industry. Only exceptional men give rise to legend: seventy years after his successful submission of sheet-glass to the judgment of the Society in the Adelphi, the *Birmingham Journal* was telling the tale of his adventures in Germany and Bohemia in search of the secret of sheet-glass manufacture; as Richard Foley had fiddled his way to Sweden more than a century previously and brought back the secret of the slitting-mill, so George Ensell had fiddled his to Germany and returned possessed of the secret he had so dangerously sought. If there was drama in the Foley saga, there was melodrama in the Ensell story in which the English spy had been caught, sentenced to death and had escaped.

By 1774 George Ensell was in sole possession of the Coalbournbrook glass-house; on the 'Plan for a Navigable Canal from Stourbridge to the Canal from the Trent to the Severn near Stourton and Collateral-Branches to the Coal Mines upon Pensnett Chase' made in that year by Robert Whitworth, two glass-houses are shown at Coalbournbrook, 'Mess. Ensell & Hill's Glass Houses'; when Thomas Hill, who already owned one of these bought the other in 1779, the deed of sale refers to it as being 'now held by the said George Ensall (sic)'. It was here that he carried on his manufacture of sheet-glass, a natural development of the old broad-glass trade, and here he perfected a new tunnel type of lehr.[3]

[1] W. A. Thorpe, S. E. Winbolt and D. N. Sandilands all state this.

[2] In the Ashwood Hay Inclosure Award, 1776, Charles Ensell appears as 'Charles Insall'.

[3] Sandilands writes that George Ensell built the 'first' lehr for annealing; see Merret's description (1662) of the 'leer', page 76.

The Langford list of glass manufacturers in the Stourbridge district in 1760 shows that of the ten glass-houses then at work three only were still producing that glass which had been the industry's initial product—broad-glass, the three manufacturers being named as 'Pidcock Hill Rodgers', that is, the houses were the Dial, one of the Coalbournbrook pair and Holloway End. Broad-glass was falling further out of favour, not only here but in the other glass centres, Newcastle, Bristol and London. As early as 1703 Neve had reported that the Woolwich broad-glass makers 'do not now make there'; by 1712 a Bristol house was making crown-glass and in 1728 crown had come to this district, and was being made at Dennis. Crown had driven broad practically out of the market by the end of the century in a new Norman Conquest.

But Thomas Henzey's dream was to come true; broad-glass was on its way back. The purchase of the British Crown Glass Company's works at Smethwick by Robert Lucas Chance in 1824 sounded the knell of crown at a time when it was the only kind of window-glass being made or used in England. Eight years later, in collaboration with the French glassman Georges Bontemps, he brought French and Belgian sheet-glass makers to Smethwick; the name 'sheet-glass' could not hide the fact that this new glass with which the 'Crystal Palace' of the Great Exhibition of 1851 was to be wholly glazed was but the old broad writ large.

As we have seen, fifty-four years before the new foreigners brought their secrets to Smethwick, George Ensell had forestalled them at Coalbournbrook. His premature attempt to restore the rightful heir of the window-glass dynasty in this district merits our attention as much as it did the Adelphi Society's premium in 1778. He did not confine his activities to Coalbournbrook[1] nor plough too lonely a furrow; Robert Honeyborne, 'gent and white glass-maker of Moor Lane' joined forces with him and it was probably the business-like Honeyborne who suggested they should offer crown as well as sheet-glass; customers found this notice in the July 3 issue of the *Birmingham Gazette* in 1780:

'German sheet and crown glass. Honeyborne and Ensell having established a manufactory of German sheet and crown glass near Stourbridge beg leave to inform the public that

---

[1] Nor had the firm's activities been confined to window-glass; in 1769 a runaway apprentice, a Wordsley youth, was being advertised for; 'Samuel Richards apprentice to Pidcock Ensell & Bradley to the glass-engraving business.' Only one earlier reference to engraving here is known: in 1767 Samuel Benedict, an engraver of glass, was declared bankrupt.

PLATE 50.   A Dennis Chandelier.

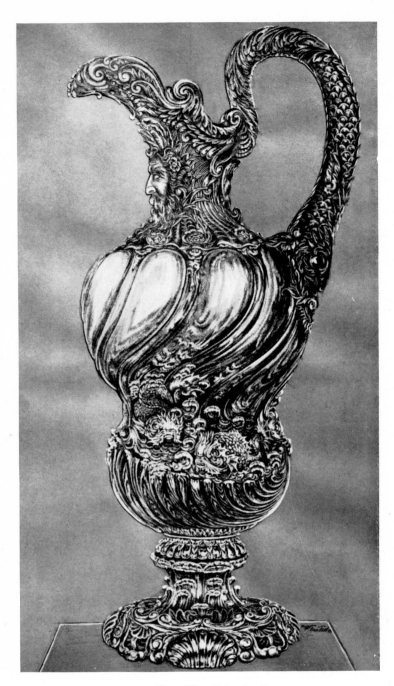

PLATE 51.   The Fritsche Ewer.

they may be supplied with any quantity on the shortest notice and upon the most reasonable terms.'

This manufactory was almost certainly the 'glasshouse, potrooms, storerooms & other conveniences at Brierley Hill very near to the turnpike road leading from Stourbridge to Dudley' which had been advertised 'To be let' in 1771 by Thomas Seager. In 1776,[1] Honeyborne & Company were working this house in Moor Lane. The short notice and reasonable terms offered did not ensure the success of the project of which no more seems to be known. It may have collapsed as Ensell's Coalbournbrook house certainly did in 1785; 'this house of Mr. George Ensell at Coalbournbrook', reported the *Worcester Journal* on 6 October, 'fell almost entirely in ruins to the ground.' This news item concluded more hopefully: 'the damage we understand will not be so great as was at first apprehended.' Whatever its extent, the damage was not fatal to Ensell's glass-making activities; he is mentioned as still a glass-maker in a list of 1789.[2]

The name 'Ensell' persisted in the trade until the eighteen-thirties,[3] not at Coalbournbrook but at Wordsley; the 1796 list of local glass-houses mentions first two Wordsley houses run by 'Bradley & Ensell'. In that year 'Richard Bradley Esq. eminent glass manufacturer near Stourbridge' died, leaving 'all my free-hold and leasehold tenements Glass Houses situate at Wordsley' to 'Mary Bradley, Kitty Bradley and Lucy Mary Ensall'. Mary Bradley was his 'dear mother', Kitty his sister and Lucy Ensall his niece. These three women were the 'Messrs. Bradley & Ensell' of the 1796 list, who 'returned thanks' in the *Birmingham Gazette*, 'for all favours conferred on their late worthy relation Richard Bradley' and hoped 'for continuance. The Glass and Coal[4] trade will be carried on with the same punctuality and despatch as usual'. The works were managed by Charles Ensell the Elder while Charles Junior and Richard Bradley Ensell were in charge of the administrative side of the business. Obviously the family relationship of the Ensells with Richard Bradley was as

[1] The Ashwood Hay Inclosure Award gives this. The house was later to become Stevens & Williams' first glass-house. It was on land belonging to the Seagers (a family commemorated in Seager's Lane) who probably built the glass-house. 'John Seager, Glassman' is mentioned in the Kingswinford Parish Register in 1720.

[2] Wakefield says that he was bankrupt in 1786 at The Holly Hall Glassworks (Green's).

[3] A 'G. Ensell' was advertising in the *Birmingham Post* in 1858 as a dealer in glass wares of all kinds.

[4] Richard Bradley's collieries were at Brockmoor.

close as the trade association. An Ensell had married Phoebe Bradley, Richard's sister; this was not Charles, who married a Mary Biven, but probably George.

Richard Bradley, a much more successful businessman than any of his Audnam namesakes had been, had been making glass at Wordsley since before 1775; the site of his first glass-house is shown on the Canal plan of that year on the north bank of the proposed cut and on the west side of the Stourbridge–Wolverhampton road. Later he bought that piece of land adjoining his glass-house premises called the Park with the Park House[1] from John Northall. On the opposite side of the road he built a second glass-house, soon to become a bottle-house, and it may have been his building of this that was the point at issue when he was presented at the Manorial Court in 1787; the Court Rolls report that

> 'We amerce Richard Bradley glassmaker in the sum of 1.19.11 for a Nuisance in having erected a Brick Wall or Building upon the Kings Highway at Wordsley.'

Richard was ordered to remove his nuisance on pain of forfeiting a further £1 19s. 11d.[2]

Immediately after Richard's death, 'Messrs. Bradley & Ensell' took one of the Pagetts (Pachett), old Wordsley broad-glass makers, as partner in the bottle-house. When Lucy Ensall married John Holt of Wigan, the firm was reorganized, Charles Ensell joining the partners, as 'Bradley, Ensell & Holt'. It was under this title that in 1801 it was advertising in the *Birmingham Gazette* for

> '3 or 4 overhand glass cutters'.

When John Holt died, his interest in the business came to his heiress Mary and her name appears in the handbook to the Fowler 1822 map of the Kingswinford Parish as owner of the lands attached to the works and some of the premises, including Park House in which she lived and part of which was used as the works' offices. Mary married George William Wainwright who, though 'of London' came of a Dudley family. Richard Bradley had made 'my friend Joseph Wainwright of Dudley Surgeon' an executor by his will and it was this Dr. Wainwright who was appointed 'Apothecary of the Poor' by the Kingswinford Vestry in 1803 'with a Salary of Twenty Pounds for the Year'.[3] A dissolution

[1] Often called to-day mistakenly 'Wordsley Manor House'.

[2] The Court's maximum penalty.

[3] The *Universal British Directory* of 1793 names Richard Bradley as one of ten 'Stourbridge' glass-makers.

Among the signatures of the 'principal inhabitants' who really constituted

of partnership in 1827 left Richard Bradley Ensell as sole proprietor; two years later according to *Pigot's Commercial Directory*, there were three glass-houses being worked by the family, one by 'Ensell's Executors', a second by 'Ensell & Co.' and the third by George William Wainwright, the last two making 'plain and cut glass'. A Parliamentary return of 1833 gives two names only, R. B. Ensell and Sarah Ensell, that is, the son of the sole proprietor of 1827 and his widowed mother.

Despite these bewildering changes of ownership within the family—Bradley, Ensell, Bradley-Ensell, Holt, Wainwright in various combinations—the gaffer in his chair, the bottle-maker at his brass mould, the cutter at his wheels, worked on in the three houses, producing 'plain and cut and bottles' and the firm, whatever its title, paid over to the Exchequer its two to three hundred pounds Duty per round throughout. The coming of 'Thomas Webb & Co.' (the family still represented by a Wainwright) meant only a master with a different name to the workman and the public at the time; now we can see the significance of the change, for with the new ownership came in the Richardsons. By 1833, the firm had become 'Messrs. Webb & Richardson'. The Glass Licence for the works issued on 5 July 1838

> 'licensed and empowered Wm. Haden Richardson, Benjamin Richardson and Jonathan Richardson to exercise or carry on the Trade or Business of Glassmakers at Wordsley, they having paid the sum of £20. 0. 0.'

At the 'Great Exhibition of the Works of Industry of all Nations' held under the presidency of 'His Royal Highness Prince Albert, K.G.', under the roof of the 'Crystal Palace' which was glazed with that sheet-glass, the manufacture of which George Ensell had valiantly attempted to establish at Coalbournbrook seventy years previously, Messrs. Richardson were awarded a Prize Medal not for 'plain and cut and bottles' but for 'cut crystal, opal vases painted with enamel colours (the Judgment of Paris, the Dream of Penelope, Aesop's Fables &c. &c), opal glass

---

the theoretically open-to-all Vestry at this time, those of the following glass-men constantly appear: Michael Coltman, Wm. Grafton, John Pidcock, Thos. & P. Wheeley, Charles Ensell, Thos. & John Honeyborne, John Holt, Michael Grazebrook. These with the addition of Bradley & Co., Wordsley and Wheeley & Littlewood appear also among the 254 signatures to a resolution passed at a meeting at the Talbot, 11 July 1803, 'to agree to accept notes of Stourbridge bankers to prevent Alarm or want of Confidence in Holders of Country Bank notes'. 'Thomas Wainwright of Dudley Surgeon' was named as commissioner in the Dudley Road Act of 1747.

ornamented with Pet Fawn in enamel colours, Grecian figures in coloured enamels'. Their exhibit so pleased the President's Royal spouse, Queen Victoria, that she commanded Henry Cole, according to a letter Richardson's received in July 1851,

> 'to desire that you will send a similar glass to that numbered 301 in your Stall with a venetian foot to Buckingham Palace'.

The *Birmingham Journal* had anticipated Her Majesty's appreciation of the Wordsley gaffers' artistry with this testimonial on 31 May:

> 'Messrs. Richardson of Wordsley are well entitled to precedence, the purity of their flint has no equal in the Exhibition.'

Richard Bradley's choice of Wordsley as the site of his glass-house was a happy one. The village, built on the slopes of the Wordsley Brook's valley and lying across that same ancient highway on which already stood the Holloway End, Coalbournbrook, Dennis, Dial and Audnam houses, had been a centre of thriving industry for some hundreds of years before he followed Winsor James's example and set up his furnace there. For two centuries before the first glassmen brought their new craft into the district its nailers and scythesmiths, forgemen and hammermen had been exploiting the mineral resources of the manor and the water-power of the Stour and its tributary streams. It was the busiest and most thickly-peopled centre in the wide straggling parish of Kingswinford and retained its industrial and social pre-eminence until the rapid growth of the township of Brierley Hill in the nineteenth century shifted the centre of civic gravity; when the ancient glebe lands were sold to Lord Dudley by permission of a special Act of Parliament in 1826, it was Wordsley that was chosen as the site of the new mother church of the parish and until well past the middle of the nineteenth century the Petty Sessional Court, the Kingswinford and Wordsley Petty Sessions was held there.[1]

Richard Bradley's and Winsor James's Dob Hill glass-houses were in the village itself; Thomas Henzey's Dial and the other Bradleys' ill-starred house were at its southern boundary on the edge of Audnam Field, one of the great common fields of the village. The Dial was still busy, still producing broad-glass. The

---

[1] It was not until 1955 that, although the Court had been transferred to Brierley Hill for the best part of a century, the name was changed to the 'Brierley Hill Petty Sessional Court'.

PLATE 52.   Two Fritsche engraved glasses.

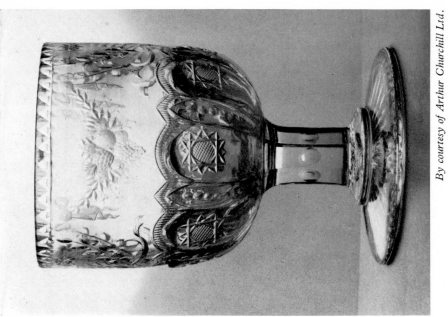

By courtesy of Arthur Churchill Ltd.

(b) Goblet engraved by W. Fritsche (Dennis) *circa* 1900.

By courtesy of A. Sanders, Esq.

PLATE 53. (a) Fritsche engraved glass.

Audnam house of Edward Bradley had come into other hands: its story is as complicated as chequered. By successive agreements it passed through the control of Jeremiah Rogers of Holloway End glass-house and Thomas Hamond of Brettell, then of Winsor James, then of Joshua Henzey. The last Bradley to work it was Henry who was declared bankrupt in 1729. A final tripartite agreement[1] between Joshua Henzey, Henry and Mary Bradley and John Ward of Sedgley Park stated that Joshua Henzey was then owed £479 10s. 7d., but that Henry Bradley was the real owner of the glass-house and could get possession of it from John Ward on the payment of £500 within six months. It was actually fifteen years later, however, in 1747, that Henry finally surrendered the house to John Ward, who had in 1740 become Lord Ward (Dudley), as mortgagee. Lord Dudley (or his agent) seems to have been peculiarly lenient to glass-makers; at the same time as he was allowing Henry Bradley's six months to spread over fifteen years, he collected no rent for twenty-three years (1743–66)[2] from Joseph Green[3] who had a glass-house at Springsmire (Scots Green) where the Dudley–Kingswinford road joins that from Dudley to Brierley Hill.

Lord Dudley let the Audnam glass-house to a Michael Grazebrook[4] at an annual rent of £50; by 1760 the house was one of two in the district producing 'smooth enamel glass' in addition to 'flint glass best and ordinary and phials'. The second house making the same variety was worked by a Denham; this was probably at Audnam too; a William Denham was occupying land next to the Audnam house in 1776.[5] In this year it was a Sarah Grazebrook who was in possession of Audnam; she was also

[1] The indenture of this agreement is among the Dudley family papers at the Dudley Reference Library.

[2] From Lord Dudley's Rent-Roll:
'1766. Feb. 28. Mr. Joseph Green for the Glasshouse Croft and House for the year 1743 to this Time being 23 Years at 22. 10. 0 p. Ann. £517. 10.0.'
The roll shows that Michael Grazebrook paid his £50 regularly year by year.

[3] 'John Green of Dudley, White glassmaker' is mentioned in the Kingswinford Court Rolls 1756.

[4] On 14 October 1650 a 'Michael Grasbrooke' was a complainant at a Court Baron of the Kingswinford Manor.

[5] The Ashwood Hay Inclosure Award.

Denham may have been working at Audnam in some form of temporary partnership with Grazebrook; the facts that both were making the same kinds of glass and their being the only two makers of 'smooth enamel' and that this is the only mention of Denham's glass-making known suggests such collaboration.

working the Dob Hill house which had come into the possession of Robert Honeyborne. Tradition tells how, as an old lady, Sarah used to sit at her bedroom window with an hour-glass to time her workmen's shifts. For a century the Grazebrooks were to work the eight-pot furnace at this house. In 1860 they transferred their industrial activities to other furnaces: the blast-furnaces and puddling-furnaces of that iron industry in which after another century they are still engaged.

Chapter 10

OLD FURNACES—NEW PRODUCTS
NEW MEN—NEW METHODS

The casual and anonymous gentleman tourist who 'saw Stourbridge before him' in 1776, 'a town eminent for its glass manufactory' and entered it to satisfy his roving curiosity, tells us more of the industry in the eighteenth century than all the directories and trade dictionaries between 1696 and 1796. What especially impressed him was the 'introducing of those beautiful spiral threads of a different colour so nicely spun within the neck of a wine glass' and the ease with which this apparently inexplicable feat was performed 'even by children', these being presumably the apprentices who were obtained from Oldswinford Hospital and the Overseers of the Poor of the neighbouring parishes. One of the glass-makers, 'a half-burnt cadaverous-looking animal' at his request fashioned him such a glass.

Doctor Pococke, who had travelled through the glass-making districts of Germany and Bohemia and knew something of its manufacture before coming to Stourbridge, 'famous for its glass manufactures', naturally expressed no such childish surprise at what he discovered here in 1751: 'coloured glass which is here coloured in the liquid of all the capital colours in their several shades . . . a secret which they have here'; in the course of a second visit he saw the rich painted Flemish glass windows in Hagley Church 'bordered with coloured glass thrown into pretty Gothic figures . . . blue purple and green glass lately made at Stourbridge', the kind of glass for making which John Hill was to hand over his recipes to Gatchell of Waterford thirty years later, 'Flint Enamel Blue & Best Green Glass'.

Equally informative in a smaller way is the prudent accountancy of the Wollescote attorney Milward, who recorded that in 1702 he exchanged his black mare for thirty-six gross of glass buttons from a Bradley; so also are Defoe's notes in the *Tradesmen* that watch-glasses were made in the district, and the merchant's account showing that 'cruets mounted with Stourbridge glass' were imported into Belfast in 1754.

'Here are about ten glasshouses', stated the *Travellers Guide* in 1805, 'where are made drinking-glasses, bottles and window-glass.' This seems only to repeat Houghton's 'window-glass bottles flint' in his 1696 list of English glass-houses and to suggest a century and more without expansion or development. Indeed the drop in numbers from Houghton's seventeen to the 'about ten' in the *Guide* seems to support that suggestion; Houghton's too simple arithmetic, however, had not allowed for the fact that some of the glass-houses here were making two or more kinds of glass, flint and bottles or flint and window-glass, and these he counted twice. All the directories and trade dictionaries of the eighteenth century give the number of houses in the district as 'ten' or 'about ten'.

Houghton's 'window-glass' had a much narrower meaning than the one given in the *Guide*; in 1696 'window-glass' here meant broad-glass only, in 1805, the name covered broad, crown and sheet, plain and coloured. Houghton's bottles had been serving-bottles,[1] cider bottles, phials and cordials for apothecaries but the century preceding the *Guide* had added such refined products as scent bottles in opaque-white and blue glass. Houghton's 'flint' meant wines, ales, beer goblets, the *Guide* 'drinking glasses' were of the different shapes dictated by the increased cost of metal under the Excise duties and the passing fashions which had also influenced those of silver, of the new porcelain, of furniture and buildings: and the advent of the grinders, cutters and engravers, had substituted decoration for ornament.

A new craftsman, the decorator, had invaded the industry; the gaffer no longer produced the finished product; the end of the lehr was now not the terminus but only an intermediate station; for the future the glass-house was to be only one department of a glass-works, the finished article was to come from the cutting-shop.

What was the reaction of the glass-maker to his dethronement? The gentlemen-glaziers of the sixteenth and seventeenth centuries 'compelled to work in their shirts like Cyclopes', the 'half-burnt cadaverous-looking animal' whose cunning so dazzled the tourist in 1776, the 'pale thin-faced slender white-glass servitor', all prided themselves on their 'power of creating the beautiful, to see as it were the mere thought of their minds create a beautiful article of use or ornament by the breath of their mouths expanding

---

[1] The early serving-bottles were shapely enough and of that brownish-green hue so much more pleasing to the eye than the rather insipid new flint glass.

the ductile material till it attains the shape that they desire'; so wrote one of them years later in words as lame as his craft was agile. These gaffers, master-workmen, had now perforce to pass on their 'beautiful articles' to the grinders, unwelcome intruders, who, poisoning themselves with putty-powder and red lead and deafening their ears with the screams of their wheels, worked first in a wrought-iron mill on the Stour, then in separate establishments, and finally in 'cutting-shops' on the same premises as the gaffers' eternal furnace-fires. They were not glassmen but came from London shops and shops there meant hucksters' shops not workshops as here. The gaffers were Ruskinians before Ruskin was born.

To the glass-maker, given a metal of satisfying texture and colour, shape was all; his natural aversion to any tampering with his shape prevented his seeing for many a long year that cutting in moderation could add a further beauty to the vessel he had brought into being. While this prejudice remained there could be no craft-fellowship between maker and cutter, and therefore no real integration of design, of the gaffer's shape and the cutter's pattern; that prejudice developed intensity with each new demand the cutters made, for naturally enough these exploited the possibilities of their new technique to the full; they began to cut deeper and deeper so that the glass-makers were called upon for thicker and thicker vessels and these lost that 'diaphonous daintiness' which used so to delight the young James Howell. Here the glass-maker had a real grievance: he was under contract to make so many vessels of a sort each 'move' or turn of six hours and, when the heavier vessel was ordered, was still expected to make the same number; his economic objection to this was further strengthened by an aesthetic one, for the cutters now spread their patterns further and further over the surface of the vessel until this was covered and the gaffer saw the beautiful flowing lines of his shapes broken and bent into stuttering outlines.

Still the new technique brought the glass-makers some compensation in a new appeal to their craft-cunning, the casing of their flint-glass vessels with one of the new coloured glasses and it was the less objectionable of the new workmen, the under-hand cutter, the engraver with his copper wheel, who at first did most of the decoration on these, a shallow grinding of the surface in pattern just deep enough to get through the coloured casing to the flint beneath; the over-hand grinders, the cutters, added their contribution but this working in harness checked their normal abuse of the wheel. The variety of new forms fashion demanded also put the gaffers on their mettle; the new taper decanters and cruets, the tall skittle-like bottles in their different pot-coloured metals, the rummers with their short stems, the tankards.

A priced bill of 1804 in the Palfrey Collection lists some of the products of the Moor Lane Glass-house,[1] then being worked by Honeyborne and Batson: 'Square foot Ales fluted and hollows and foot cut; Gills cut and puntyed; Gills fluted and puntyed; Wines fluted; Pint and Quart Decanters cut to pattern; Round foot Goblets fluted puntyed and Shanked; Canns fingered and Cut handles; Wines fluted; Coolers fingered; Mustard pots; Decanters slopes and fingered.'

The square, like the oval and diamond, was for that fashion's fleeting life used for all glass feet; moulded, of course, not blown, it was sometimes domed underneath. The punty marks were ground off, not to return until glass-makers here began to supply a demand for 'antiques'.[2]

The Moor Lane firm was supplying these to J. Dovey and Son, who were themselves glass-cutters; thirty-two years previously James Dovey had been advertising in the *Birmingham Gazette* for 'a youth about 13 or 14 as an apprentice to a glasscutter'. He was then working at Wollaston Mill on the Stour brank opposite to Hill and Waldron's blade-mill on the premises of their Coalbournbrook glass-houses and was using water-power in place of boy-power; previously it had been a boy's job to turn the cutter's wheels from the end of the shop, a no less tiring occupation than the alternative bellows-blowing in the nailshops adjoining. About 1790, Dovey (with John Benson of the Priory, Dudley) first introduced a steam-driven plant which soon became general.[3] In 1801, Bradley Ensell and Holt were asking for 'three or four good overhand glasscutters' and then for 'several good workmen that can work over-handed' and promising such men 'liberal wages and full employment'.

Nothing which can be certainly labelled 'Stourbridge Glass' of

---

[1] It is interesting to note that this bill is headed 'Stourbridge' although the glasshouse was three miles away in Brierley Hill.

[2] Thirty years ago a Wordsley firm carried on a thriving trade in 'heavy antiques'—arch-ribbed goblets with merese stems, decorated with vine leaves and barley heads: the punty mark was left unground to prove the goblet's 'antiquity'.

[3] One record claims that 'John Dovey of Brettell Lane was the first to use wrought iron mills for cutting glass' and to have introduced 'the double mitre and double-hollow stones'.

this period remains known as evidence of the industry's achievement. This 'amorphous solid', as a physicist has called it, though of such toughness that a diamond must be used to cut it, is yet so fragile that a violin note (or an operatic tenor's), vibrating at the same frequency, can shatter it. The vessel that in a sealed tomb could outlast millennia, succumbs to momentary carelessness or a drop of hot water. That fragility which is not the least of its beauties practically ensures its destruction; only a church window provides reasonable chance of longevity. The fact that in a glass-making district a broken vessel could so easily be replaced, the fact that abundance, even of beauty, kills wonder and appreciation, the fact that the Excise regulations allowed a percentage of broken glass, cullet, free of the tax on raw materials, to be used in a batch with the result that not only accidental waste was used but vessels of outmoded fashions were deliberately destroyed for this purpose, and the lack of trade-marks—all these help to explain the absence of any material evidence. The showroom in which mere inertia or a gradually developing historical interest might have preserved specimens for posterity was yet to come and, in most cases, the manufacturers were businessmen with a keener eye for balance sheets than for formal or other beauty.

Other than the few and brief travellers' tales we have only the equally few but less explicit records in directories or trade dictionaries; these give usually names of manufacturers, occasionally the particular product of a house is mentioned, one lists the number of pots in each glass-house. In all the lists the number of houses at work is given as 'ten', 'about ten' or 'about half a score'. The first list and most informative, Langford's, dates from 1760 and is included in an appendix to the second volume of *Staffordshire and Warwickshire, Past and Present*: 'the glass manufacture of the Stourbridge district in 1760 was in the hands of the following producers'; ten names are given, all but three of whom were making more than one kind of glass. Two manufacturers, Grazebrook and Denham,[1] appear as makers of 'smooth enamel glass', that is, the new 'opaque white' glass which had reached this district from Bristol where the Amblecote Littles were making it. Three houses, the Dial, Holloway End and one of the Coalbournbrook pair, were still producing the old broad-glass and bottles; 'flint glass best and ordinary' was coming from Audnam Bank, from Richard Bradley's Wordsley house, the second Coalbournbrook house, Holloway End, Moor Lane, the Heath and the

[1] Denham. See note, page 103.

glass-house being worked by the Little, still in this district; phials were being fashioned at the Dial, Audnam, Coalbournbrook, Holloway End, the Heath and Moor Lane.

The most valuable item of information here is that first mention of the manufacture in this district of the enamel glass which was so much like porcelain, 'opaque-white' glass, made famous especially by the products of Jacob Little's 'White Flint Glasshouse' at Bristol. Its likeness to porcelain was no accidental coincidence, the same tin oxide was used for both and porcelain was being made at Bristol as early as 1750. Now Stourbridge and Bristol had for more than a century known very well what each other was doing and Stourbridge may actually have been producing the new porcelain at as early a date if not earlier. An attempt had certainly been made before 1751 to set up a porcelain factory here. Dr. Pococke's account of his visit in that year tells us:

> 'They had also a manufacture of china with a contract to sell it only to the promoters of it in London, but I found it not carried on.'

The enamel-glass houses produced the same shapes as the porcelain factories and these were decorated in the same manner and often by the same workmen, with painted birds, flower sprays, ribbon and wreath borders, landscapes. It is not known if the Stourbridge ware was decorated here or sent as blanks to the decorators in Birmingham and London, where, since the establishment of the Bow and Chelsea porcelain factories, demand for it had quickly grown. The vogue for enamelled trinkets, snuff-boxes and the like tempted also the metal-workers of Bilston into production; this was carried on for seventy years, there being no less than eighteen 'masters' in the trade there in 1760.

This 'white flint', 'opake white glass' or 'enamel glass' seems to have been known as early as the sixteen-sixties, for an item in the London Glass Sellers' List was a beer glass, 'speckled enameld'.[1] In 1691 there is a reference to 'The art of Painting[2] with the New Invention of Spot Dyals'. According to Dossie's *Handmaid to the Arts*, 'opake white glass' was being made near London in 1758, and 'enamel plates and dials were made there'. Now in 1747, the lease of the glass-house built by Thomas Henzey in 1704, worked by the third Joshua Henzey, and then by his

---

[1] 'Speckled enameld' was being made here as late as thirty years ago for ornamental electric light shades; white glass on the end of the blowing iron was dipped into a 'frost' of mixed colours.

[2] 'Painting'—painting on glass.

(b) Decanter 'Hunting the Eagle'
engraved by F. E. Kny.

PLATE 54. (a) Vase engraved by F. E. Kny.

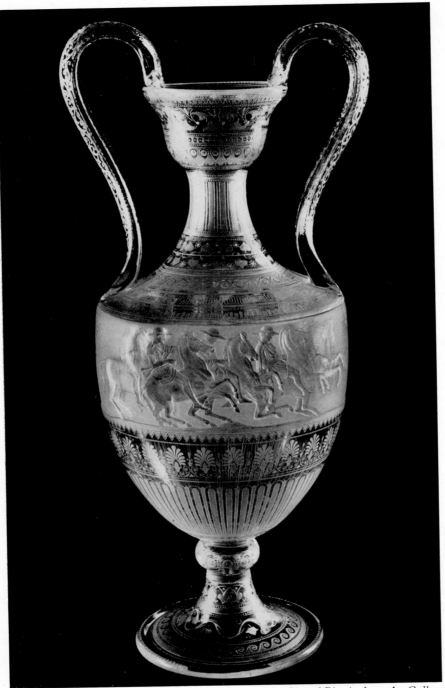

PLATE 55.   The 'Elgin' Vase.   John Northwood, 1873.

nephews John Pidcock and John Godwin, was advertised for sale: 'To be sold the remainder of a lease (56 years) of the Dyal Glass-House.'

This is the first known mention of this house by that name which became, and still is, so well known.[1] There is no reason why it should have been so called unless dials were made there and little doubt that these were of opaque white glass. Although Langford's list gives only broad-glass, bottles and phials as its products in 1760 it cannot be assumed, as we shall see, that the Dial was no longer making this new glass. The Heath glass-house is credited only with flint and phials. In the letter describing his misadventure with the elegant wine-glass which had been made for him, the 1776 tourist does not state at what glass-house he received this gift, but it was almost certainly the Heath; he was on his way from Stourbridge town to Kinver Edge and immediately after leaving the glass-house he crossed 'an extensive chearful common' before dropping into the 'delicious valley at Stewponey'.

He had come to Stourbridge only just in time, for the new tax on enamel in the next year practically put an end to these twists. So apparently difficult a feat could actually be, as he saw there, performed even by young apprentices. Canes of coloured glass were arranged in a designed series round the inside of a cylindrical mould; a blob of metal thrust into the mould picked up the canes which were then twisted, covered and drawn out into a long rod. More elaborate twists were made by combining groups of these rods and repeating the twisting and drawing out.

Work seems to have been carried on rather spasmodically at the Heath; we last noted it as put up for sale by the Commissioners of Bankruptcy in 1736; the premises had then been mortgaged for at least nine years to William Penn of Harborough.[2] In 1752 this mortgage was paid off and Edward Russell the Younger took over. Russell may have learned something of the glass trade with Thomas Rogers at Holloway End;[3] by 1769 he was 'owner of the Heath Glasshouse . . . a wealthy glass manufacturer'. Dying in 1778, Russell left his property to his three nephews, Francis Witton, Richard Russell Witton and Serjeant[4]

---

[1] The present Dial Glasshouse is the New Dial built in 1887 on a site not far distant from the old.

[2] Grandfather of William Shenstone the poet.

[3] The Holloway End house was 'to let' in 1768; enquiries to be made to Thomas Rogers or Edward Russell.

[4] 'Serjeant' commemorates his descent from Richard Serjeant, well-known

Witton; it was the third of these who worked the now century-old nine-pot house until he became bankrupt in 1801. The Ruffords followed; they had other interests, particularly and fatefully banking; during the eighteen-thirties a Walker joined them and it was Walkers who, carrying on after the Rufford bank failed in the middle of the century, went out with the last fire at the Heath furnace in 1882; but not before they had attracted customers as distant and eminent as the Sultan of Turkey for whom they had made a cut-glass chandelier which cost him £10,000. The first of the magnificent series of such lustres made in the Stourbridge district dates (according to Thorpe) from as early as 1760. Bradley, Ensell and Holt certainly made one and kept it on show at Wordsley for many years.

At some time about 1770, after more than a century of financially successful glass-making at Holloway End, the Rogers left the district and the trade for London and banking. The family had acquired the 'spacious brick mansion approached by a long and lofty avenue of sycamores' on the summit of the hill opposite and overlooking their works, a house probably built by John Grove who was living there in 1724.[1] It was this house, 'The Hill', now the Corbett Hospital, that they left for Cornhill. The exodus of the Welsh Rogers made way for the entry of a remarkable Scot, James Keir. The seventeenth century title of 'ingenious gentleman' was by this time obsolete, but Keir was the type, always more interested in the technology than the practice of the craft. Medical student, soldier with service (as Captain in the 61st Foot) in Ireland, France and the West Indies, Fellow of the Royal Society and of the Royal Astronomical Society, contributor to scientific journals and 'eminent philosopher', he used the old glass-house as 'the laboratory wherein some of his ingenious experiments were conducted'. He exploited the results of these in allied and other industries, the manufacture of alkali, soap and red-lead at Tipton, iron-works at Soho, collieries at Tividale; his youthful military experiences fired him to take an active part in quelling the Priestley riots in Birmingham in 1791, and as an Amblecote ratepayer three years later, he had to pay his share of the 'thirty seven pounds six shillings and ten pence halfpenny' which was the parish's 'proportion of the Damages recovered

---

as one of the Bartholomew Divines ejected from their livings in 1662. The Nettlefolds and Chamberlains of Birmingham were also descended from Serjeant.

[1] Kingswinford Court Rolls: 'John Grove of le Hill Amblecote.'

against the Hundred for the late Riots in Birmingham and its Neighbourhood'. During the later years of his association with Holloway End, the glass-house was worked by a company, Scott, Keir, Jones & Co.[1]

After the long tenure of Holloway End by the Rogers,[2] a family with a glass-making tradition and Lorrainer blood, there were many changes in ownership to come; the day of the maker-owner had gone, businessmen not craftsmen were now almost everywhere in control. A temporary return to the old practice was tried about 1800 by two Wordsley glass-cutters, James and Thomas Parrish, but by 1803 they were bankrupt.

From 1779, both Coalbournbrook houses belonged to Thomas Hill, the 'Squire' of Dennis Park, living in Dennis House. Traditionally a scythesmith, he preferred to be known as 'Ironmaster' and made no attempt to rebuild the ruined Dennis glass-house within his grounds; however, he put the bricks from it to good use, building with them the first school at the Lye. The partners of the 'Hill and Waldron' firm working the glass-houses were Thomas Hill's father, Waldron Hill, Thomas himself and William Waldron. The Waldrons were scythesmiths, too, so it is not surprising to find that they had a blade-mill on the Stour which bounded their premises nor can one wonder at the nailshops clustered about the glass-house cones.[3] The partners were 'Jacks' of all the local trades and glass to them was merely one of these; scythes, knives of all kinds, nails, firebricks were as much to them as the bottles, phials and flint-glass their two glass-houses produced; it is difficult to believe that, while they continued for some time to produce that sheet-glass which George Ensell had introduced there, they took any pride in the fact that they were continuing a tradition, that this was the glass the Lorrainers had come to make nearly two centuries previously. They prospered into banking.

Among the names appearing as those of partners here at various reshufflings are Littlewood and Wheeley; here again were men for whom glass-making was only one item in a full programme of industrial activities. A Littlewood and a Wheeley were partners

[1] One of Keir's partners here was Samuel Skey of Bewdley, who pirated patents, was dry salter, and manufacturer of vitriol and dyes and drove about in a carriage drawn by six milk-white mules.

[2] The Thomas Rogers who left the Hill had two sons, Daniel, named after the first Thomas's Lorrainer father-in-law, Daniel Tittery, and Samuel, banker and poet.

[3] There was also a 'Firebrick manufactory' on the premises.

for a time working the old glass-house of the first Joshua Henzey at Brettell Lane. The Littlewoods followed the Keir regime at Holloway End and were financially interested at least in Coalbournbrook; they mined fireclay at Brettell Lane[1] and regularly exported it to Waterford in ten-hundredweight casks at 95s. per ton; they made firebricks, they were shareholders in country banks; they married substance and the last sons graduated into the Established Church as parsons.

The Wheeleys were as variously engaged; closely connected with the Seagers of Brierley Hill, glassmen and potters, and with the Hills of Coalbournbrook, glassmen and ironmasters, they farmed wide lands in Brettell Lane and Amblecote, mined fireclay and coal, manufactured firebricks, set up a red-lead manufactory in Brettell Lane, which they later converted into an iron foundry[2] and from this laid a mineral railroad along the valley of the Delph (Coalbourn) Brook to wharves at Coalbournbrook. The latest Wheeleys, two bachelor brothers, took over Dennis House and Park from Thomas Hill[3] and conducted a prosperous export business in glass from their Brettell Lane Glass-house until they fell foul of an Excise man who considered that their method of exploiting the rebate of tenpence per pound on glass for export (packing their glass with their own firebricks) was not an excusable example of that 'questionable fraud' which manufacturers complained the incidence of the duties drove them to practice. The authorities agreed with their officer that the fraud was without question and their defence of the revenue meant the failure of the Wheeleys.

The other old Brettell Lane glass-house, Jeremy Bague's and Thomas Hamond's, a nine-pot furnace housed in what must have been one of the most capacious cones in the country,[4] was being worked by Coltman and Grafton, a partnership typical of the times between a business man and a practical glass-maker who acted as works' manager. Grafton came of a family of Wordsley glass-makers; another Grafton, probably a brother, was similarly engaged at the Longport Glass-works in partnership with Thomas

[1] Littlewood King & Co.; to-day George King Harrison.

[2] Later 'Roberts & Cooper' Ironworks; to-day one of the machine-shops of Samuel Taylor and Sons.

[3] The Wheeleys had close connections with Thomas Hill; in 1796 Thomas Wheeley and Thomas Hill were devisees of the will of William Seager, Wheeley's father-in-law. Thomas Hill retired from Dennis to Blaenavon, Monmouth where he died in 1827; he appointed 'Mr. Robert Wheeley of Blaenavon' as his executor.

[4] In its notice of Thomas Hamond's death the *Craftsman* referred to him as the owner of a *great* glass-house near Birmingham.

PLATE 56. 'Elgin' Claret Jug. F. E. Kny. 1873.

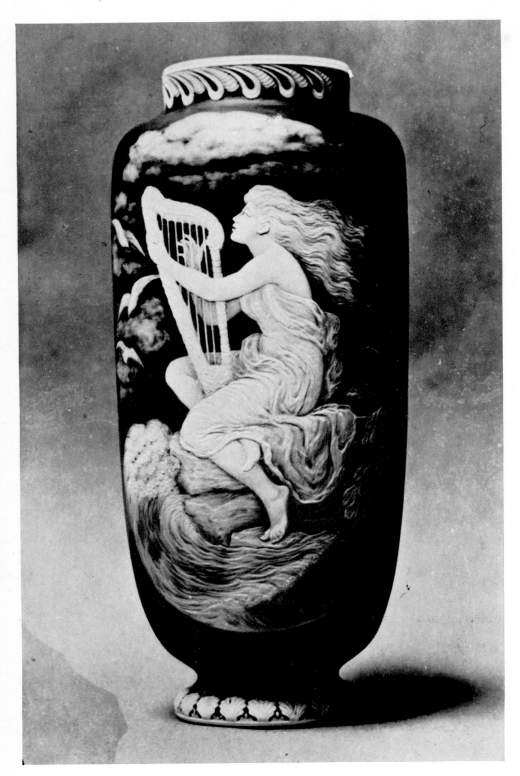

PLATE 57.   'Siren' Vase.   George Woodall.

Kinnersley and John Davenport, Kinnersley a business man and Davenport the well-known potter.[1]

Only at Audnam, 'Audenham Bank Glass House', where the Grazebrooks, successively Michael, Sarah, Grazebrook and Sons, M. and W. Grazebrook, persisted in sole possession was there no such Paul Jones shuffling of partners as took place at the other houses. At the Dial, the only house where the Lorrainers, in their descendants the Pidcocks and in the broad-glass produced there, still held sway, the early years of the nineteenth century brought in a Cope[2] who had been a partner in the Wrockwardine (Salop) Glass-house, William Henry Cope, who came to live in Coal-bournhill House. The Pidcocks had a bottle warehouse in London, managed by a Benjamin Godwin (Henzey blood and Christian name); they, too, had ventured into the allied trades of fireclay-mining and firebrick-making at the Lye. Later Pidcocks took commissions in the Army and died unmarried, remained spinsters into their nineties or, abandoning glass, squired it at Platts House and served on the Commission of the Peace for the two neighbouring counties, Staffordshire and Worcestershire. Mary married a Homfray, himself also of Henzey blood but an iron-master.

During the whole of the century-old Excise period, the manu-facturers continued their Jeremiad just as they had done during the War-tax years, 1695–9: the industry was tottering to ruin. Now businessmen may flock to a feast but not like vultures to carrion; a moribund concern would never have attracted the constant stream of new men who entered the industry. And they were businessmen who had seen others retiring from the trade to become bankers, squires, landed gentlemen, clergymen, army officers or to enter larger scale industries, and sought a fortune for themselves; they were not knights-errant fighting to rescue a dis-tressed trade; they had no especial interest in glass, no tradi-tional attachment to it as had the Grazebrooks and the Honey-bornes. But, if none of them were heirs to such a tradition, some of them were destined to found one of their own, for among the new names of the early nineteenth century were Webb, Richard-son and Stevens.

[1] A Thomas Kinnersley had married Penelope Wheeler of Wollaston Hall. A widow, she was in possession of Edward Bradley's Audnam glass-house in 1761 and sold it to John Pidcock and two others.

[2] But not a 'Broad' as stated by so many writers quoting from an 1818 Directory. 'Broad' was surely a printer's error, making a personal name of 'broad', the kind of glass being produced there.

Just before the Excise duties were taken off, an 1840 Worcestershire directory was telling that 'at present the glass industry gives very profitable employment to a great number of people'; a Survey of the county in 1810 had referred to 'some good fortunes' which had been made in it. 'There was a duty on glass,' wrote an old glass-maker in his reminiscences in 1899, 'and its incidence was to raise the price much more than the actual impost'; and here are the Richardsons, in announcing the repeal of the ruinous exactions of the Exchequer, warning their customers that the removal of the duty 'cannot influence the price of Flint and Cut Glass to any extent' and that they were 'reducing the prices of the leading articles of the trade' by one penny per pound only.

While this general prosperity prevailed in the industry, how were the workmen faring, the men who actually made 'every sort of article from the simple phial or salt to most costly and elaborate chandeliers or gold enamel services'? There were, an 1841 record states, 2334 of them employed, a figure which was supposed to emphasize the fact that there was still a shortage of labour, a shortage which the manufacturers were expecting would continue. One of them, giving evidence before the Commissioners of Excise in 1833, had said: 'The removal of the duty perhaps would not be attended with such advantages as some persons seemed to think.' Workmen were scarce; it was difficult to acquire knowledge of the art. 'The workmen are ambitious enough and we think they would break off from establishments where they are now employed and endeavour to better themselves.' Why should the workmen want to break off from establishments which provided them with 'very profitable but not very healthy employment'? Considerations of health might tend to drive out the glass-cutters but not the glass-makers.

In 1776 an Act of Parliament was passed

'for the more easy and speedy recovery of small debts within the parish of Old Swinford'.

'There are now', says its Preamble, 'and for many years past have been divers Manufactories of Iron Glass and Cloth carried on in a very large and extensive manner.' Many of the thousands constantly employed contract 'several small debts' and often refuse to pay them. These debts were not money lost by glass manufacturers playing at hazard in the Talbot Inn nor accounts owed by their wives to Stourbridge shopkeepers; they were small debts, the Act dealing only with monies ranging from one to forty shillings. Sixty-seven Commissioners were appointed, any three of whom could form a Court of Requests to try cases and give judgement; of these, twenty were actively interested in the glass industry.

Naturally there would be some glass-makers (and glass manufacturers too) who refused to pay their debts, but there would be more who could not. On 29 March 1814 Thomas Kitely, 'a glass-blower', was appealing for relief from the Parish Overseers; he had a wife and three children and was earning twelve shillings a week. In 1841, after a rise had just been given to attract new workmen, the highest weekly wage paid to a gaffer was thirty shillings plus a bonus per move which could vary between two shillings and two shillings and threepence; to a servitor, twenty-two shillings, to a footmaker twelve and to a taker-in four while the glass-cutters were getting from twenty to thirty-four shillings according to the number of hours they worked.[1] The differing rates in the glass-house illustrate the hierarchy of the chair; there was also a hierarchy of chairs: at the summit the castor-hole chair, then in descending order, the second or 'cutting' chair, the wine-glass chair and the phial chair; here again the wage diminished on the descent, the fourth chair getting less than two-thirds of the top rate.

For one of their most arduous tasks, pot-setting, the removal of an old or faulty pot from the furnace and the setting in of a new one, to perform which 'the men are often detained four hours', the workers received no pay at all; 'all hands must be present and absentees, except from illness, are severely fined'. While engaged in this, 'the worst and roughest Work in the Art', the Lorrainers of the seventeenth century used to

'Cloath themselves with a Garment made of skins in shape of a Pantaloon, which they make as wet as possible and which covers them all over except the Eyes and for them they make use of Glass to see to guide themselves'.

A glass-maker in 1849 wrote:

'The fatigue and exhaustion of the men is very great and is attended occasionally by severe falls burns or bruises, by liability to catch cold, great excitement, energetic exertion and exposure to the flame of the open furnace.'

These were not all the costs of pot-setting as this paragraph from a letter in the glass-makers' Trade Union journal in February 1853 emphasizes:

[1] Generally ten hours a day.

'However such a system as that of slaving at pot-setting was ever introduced I know not. Men must there lose more strength, his clothes must suffer more wear and tear than a whole week's work will cause him to do and all for nothing.'

'Potsetter' from Stourbridge added this comment in the following issue:

'. . . as our society does not sanction strikes it would be very easy for men when engaging for a situation to say that they would not assist at pot-setting unless they received some remuneration for it.'[1]

While the manufacturers were complaining of a shortage of labour, the glass-makers considered the labour market already overstocked, so super-saturated indeed that 'Every thinking man must shudder at the future for glassmakers'. Not every boy who entered the glass-house in the early nineteenth century at the age of eight as a taker-in was destined to reach the highest position in the hierachy of the chair; not even the cleverest and most industrious apprentice could have the certain assurance that in due time he would become a gaffer and rule his little court of servitor, footmaker, taker-in and apprentice. There could be no more gaffers than chairs and no more chairs than pots and all the pots were not always in use. Only a constantly expanding industry, the building of more and more glass-houses, could provide chairs for the potential gaffers working yet as journeymen. And from that pool of journeymen any recalcitrant, any awkwardly independent gaffer could easily be replaced. Here was an old Guild problem in an industry that had as yet only a weakling Trade Union. The Henzeys who had found no vacant chairs had turned merchant, sailor, maltster; the Dagnias had left the district to seek them in Newcastle, the Littles had gone to Bristol.

The gaffers tackled the problem in their own crude and novel way; complain as often as they might and as bitterly as they dared, they could not prevent the manufacturers from binding (for seven years) three or four times as many apprentices as the gaffers considered sufficient to supply the normal requirements of their furnace. But they could discourage the apprentice, they could make his job as unpleasant as possible, so darken the prospect that even the glory of the chair could be so dimmed as to be invisible except to the destined eye. This they set out to do.

Let us look at a gaffer's statement of his case. He made it in

---

[1] To-day pot-setting is usually done by the teazers although in some glass-houses glass-makers help; the job is a paid one.

PLATE 58. 'Wandering Star' plaque. George Woodall.

(a)

PLATE 59.   (a) Bathroom set designed by Keith Murray.

(b) Three Keith Murray pieces.

By courtesy of Stevens & Williams Ltd.

(b)

1851, the year of the Great Exhibition, when the choicest products of the Stourbridge gaffers' art were being proudly displayed before a wondering world in a Crystal Palace, fashioned of that sheet-glass which was only a modern form of the Henzey-Tyzack-Tittery-Ensell-Dial broad-glass made in the Stourbridge district for the previous two hundred years. His figures cover all the glass-houses in the United Kingdom with the unexplained exception of the Newcastle upon Tyne district: sixty-one furnaces held five hundred and twenty-nine pots, the smallest four pots only, the largest twelve; the Stourbridge furnaces varied between eight and ten. There were at work 430 gaffers, 411 servitors, 214 footmakers and 243 apprentices and the number of journeymen, all potential gaffers waiting for chairs, was 1055 and only 33 more were known to be unemployed in any capacity.

He rounds his numbers to include Newcastle: 500 gaffers, 500 chairs in the kingdom; 300 apprentices bound for seven years, that is, an annual intake of 43 boys and an annual provision of 43 journeymen by the industry. How many vacant chairs await these forty-three trained glass-makers? Ten only, from which death or retirement has removed their late occupants. Thirty-three new men every year able and ready to create 'beautiful articles for use or ornament' and denied the opportunity.

The gaffer, however, was not mourning the artist *manqué*, he was spotlighting a dangerous rival, every one of the thirty-three coveting his chair, a wide choice for any master wishing to replace him. 'Every thinking man must shudder at the future'; but cut down the number of apprentices to seventy, that is, bring ten apprentices only to the mature craftsmanship of a journeyman each year and the normal ten empty chairs are there ready to welcome them; 'then only will we be in a position to resist those who oppress us'.

The gaffer's answer to the problem was the 'foot-ale', a 'fine' or 'tribute' paid in money by the apprentice, occasionally to celebrate his achievement of some new stage in his training or periodically, at holidays: a shilling when he made his first punty, that is, the first time he took metal from the pot, a shilling the first time he blew a wine-glass foot, one at each rise of wages, another at each shifting of place. At times so many demands were made that the youth's scanty wage was wholly consumed and he had to get money from his parents or relations to add to this to be able to pay his 'footings'. The proceeds of this extortion were spent on ale for the chair; glass-making is a thirsty job (and glass-makers 'of weak and infirm Bodies, thirsty, and easily drunk', or so Libanius anciently wrote).[1] Although the Conference of the Flint Glass Makers' Society in 1851 passed a resolution abolishing foot-ales and despite the fulminations of the Society's journal in which the offending gaffers appeared as 'Bloodsuckers who sell their characters for a pint of cheap foot-ale', the practice persisted here.

It was always rare (and still is) for the ordinary boy to reach the highest rank in less than from ten to fifteen years. Commencing as a taker-in he ascended the ladder by the very widely-spaced rungs of footmaker, servitor, workman. The condition imposed by a Factory Act of 1878 that no boy under fourteen years of age must be allowed to enter the trade was greeted by this mild gaffer's comment: 'However valuable this regulation may be for health, it is doubtful if it conduces to the proficiency of future workmen'; mild, probably because the gaffer knew that the official ban would be generally disregarded; still-living gaffers gleefully boast of their guile in successfully concealing eleven-year-old boys whenever a factory inspector visited the works.

The use of this crude and cruel economic weapon, the 'foot-ale', may have had some justification in the glass-house: it was indefensible in the cutting-shop where it was nothing more than a device for obtaining free ale. The cutting-shop apprentice was bound by no such indenture as was the glass-house boy; he could earn a comparatively good wage at puntying and was therefore a more fruitful source of forced bounty; he was mulcted more often and more heavily than his fellow at the furnace by the shop steward who collected the fines: an initial ten shillings from the boy's parents on entry or he was marked for early discharge, a shilling when he puntyed his first tumbler, another when he began fluting (the first cutting job)[2] wine or tumbler. The cutter's calendar of penal occasions covered even the apprentice's behaviour out-of-doors: a half-crown demanded when he was first seen talking to a girl ('began wenching'), five shillings if caught kissing one.

As the cutters were often on piece-work, it was very difficult for the boys to get any tuition unless they paid the workman enough to compensate him for his leaving his frame, with the

[1] 'soon fudled with wine or bear' (Merret). A popular glass-house drink in this century has been 'toast-water', water in which a well-toasted piece of bread is soaking.

[2] 'Fluting the fingers' was the sort of tedious job the cutter was very willing to pass on to the boy.

(a) A Dennis jug.

By courtesy of
Thomas Webb & Sons.

(b) Centre vase.

By courtesy of
Webb Corbett Ltd.

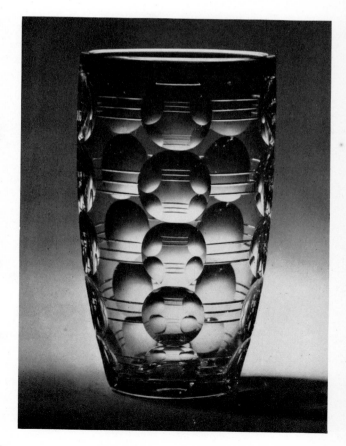

PLATE 60. (a) and (b)

PLATE 61.   Jug, tumbler and fruit bowl.

result that many finished their seven-year term nominally journey-men-cutters but possessing very little skill in cutting. Only a further payment of a sovereign ensured this pseudo-craftsman's retention in employment; even if he decided to seek his fortune elsewhere he was fined two shillings before being speeded on his uncertain way.

In one other, and a vital, particular, the unfortunate cutter's boy was infinitely worse off than the glass-maker's. However heavy the drain on his physical resources may be, the glass-maker's job was never an unhealthy one; the rheumatism and gout from which so many glass-makers in this district used to suffer were due more to their intemperate habits than to working conditions. The practice of no craft demands more ease and indeed elegance of bodily movement, none calls into use more of a man's muscles; standing, swinging, bending, blowing—all healthful activities performed in a spacious building with no noxious element in the air and hardly a sound but what the echoing hollows of the great cones tempt them to make themselves.

Mr. Horner's report of the finding of the Children's Employment Commission in 1843 made after the commissioners' visit to this district 'ventures to submit that in the event of legislative interference in the employment of children and young persons' in the glass industry certain circumstances should receive due consideration. These were that glass-makers seldom worked more than four days a week and sometimes only three; that the heat did not appear to affect the boys' health, the ventilators being ample, and that (here he was quoting the unanimous testimony of the gaffers) the prohibition of the employment of these boys, who attended beside or behind the gaffer's chair, would 'put an entire stop to work'. The boys earned an average wage of four or five shillings weekly and 'certain little gratuities were given to them for good behaviour by some glassmakers'.

Only one process was attended by any danger to health, the 'mixing and working the red lead' and 'no means of avoiding the constant injury attending the process have at present been devised . . . if the man who mixes the red lead does not lead a steady abstemious life and take medicine at regular intervals he soon dies. All become delicate if not sickly.' 'All the mixers of red lead', not the men of the chairs, not the teazers, fettling the fires; the danger was confined to the mixing-room.

The putty powder in the glass-cutting shop was all-pervading and ever-present to everybody there; as late as 1901, the average

age at death of a glass-cutter was no better than fifty-five years. In its early days glass-cutting was a separate trade from glass-making; the shops were owned by men who, in Mr. Horner's judgment, were 'respectable if not worthy'. He justifies this stricture on their worthiness by the charge that they did nothing to combat the deadly effect of the poisoned air of their shops. 'The injury from the putty-powder might be greatly lessened as the dust might be driven out of the workshop by some special ventilation but nothing has yet been attempted to obviate the injury.' Nothing even attempted. The putty powder was a mixture of oxides of lead and tin in the proportions of three and one. 'I have seen', wrote Mr. Horner, 'a boy stand with his head close over the box or trough which contained the powder so that he was constantly inhaling it while he supplied the wheel of the man who sat or stood over him and who of course had his share of the injury which however was of a less degree than that received by the boy. The putty is sure to get under the nails and if suffered to remain there a few days it often causes the hand to contract. Meals taken with unwashed hands in this condition are very injurious.'

When in 1872 the 'United Flint Glass Cutters' Society' was asking the 'Glass Masters of the Stourbridge and Wordsley District' for a nine-hour instead of the ten-hour day its members were working, to allow these men time

'for recreation and the improvement of our minds which will tend to invigorate the frame so as to enable us the better to stand our daily toil . . . (to) raise us in the social scale and better fit us for the ordinary duties of life'.

Its chairman wrote,

'There are few, if any, placed in a worse position as regards health; we are constantly in a sitting posture, breathing vitiated air, causing in consequence Dropped Hands, Cholic and almost innumerable diseases . . . there are twenty-eight members of our Trade suffering from these baneful diseases more than the whole of the districts of our Trade put together . . . Terrible, Gentlemen, is it not? . . . many of us at all ages are forced to leave the Trade through its un-healthiness.'

Until he was in the third year of his seven, the apprentice was sent out to Stourbridge town whenever the supply of powder ran short to buy the ingredients for a fresh mixture, which he was expected to make; it was he who had to pound and sieve the pumice and rotten-stone, he who had to wash the sand before this was returned to the hopper for further use; it was he who had to file the notches in the laps, the leaden wheels used for polishing chandelier drops, so that the pumice would hold to them; always taking into his adolescent lungs the impalpable poisons afloat in the stagnant air. He could not wash those lungs.

It was such men and boys, working in such conditions, many of them living in houses 'as bad as possible', who were making the wines, with welted or plain feet, with button, plain taper, thistle fancy or straw stems; the lamps, sliding and tulip, thistle, Etruscan, Grecian; the Wedgwood ink fountains; the goblets, knob, button or pulley, with thistle or ring bowl and the rest of the two hundred items of 'Glass Goods' the Flint Glass Manufacturers set out on their 1823 price list; all work-a-day stuff this. But it was also such men who were to make the elegant wine-glasses with delicately devised stems, the chandeliers, the coloured casings, the vases, the jars for scent and flowers in Egyptian, Grecian and Etruscan styles, some cut, coated gilt, painted in enamel coloured with figured ornaments, the liqueur bottles, ruby blue and green coated on flint, the ruby and opal lamp pillars for the Great Exhibition.

And at odd times they could all happily play, making friggers; in the seventeenth century James Howell had wondered at 'the diversities of shape and strange figures these curious artists will make in Glasse . . . I saw a complete Gallie with all her masts, sayles, cables, tackling . . . all made out in cristall Glasse'; Celia Fiennes had seen 'a man that spunn Glass and made several things in Glass, birds and beasts . . . I saw him make a Swan presently'. Friggering has always been the glass-maker's delight; this artistic exploration of the potentialities of his medium could lead to the glass fountain with coloured spun-tailed birds perched in a maze of overhanging arches or to a fantastic tobacco pipe, to a paper weight in which a storm of coloured snow would fall at any shaking, to a love-token in the shape of a rolling-pin or to the post-horns and musical instruments, twisted walking-sticks, the bells and bugles he carried with him in the annual parades. The boys learned much of the craft while friggering and some manufacturers in the district made them free of the glass-houses on Saturdays to work without pattern and try their prentice hands, an experiment in the play-way of education which was not to be tried in our schools until another century had passed. On work-days it was only 'by stealth or the favour of the workman' that boys who had spent two or three years as takers-in could get an opportunity of a 'little practice and become qualified as footmakers'.

Chapter 11

VICTORIANA

Magnificence was the key-note of the Exhibition in Hyde Park which was opened on May-day 1851 'by the Queen and Prince Albert in great pomp and state attended with an immense retinue of English and Foreign potentates.' The local newspaper which thus announced it proudly continued:

'Many of us denizens of the Black Country attended also and paid our respects to the immense block of coal exhibited which came from the bowels of the earth at Dudley Port.'

The 'Crystal Palace' itself, through the galleries of which they trapesed in respectful wonder was almost entirely a Black Country product; its great sheets of Smethwick glass were framed in iron from Dudley-Woodside.[1] Even if their perambulation did not persevere as far as the Central North Gallery which housed 'Class 24 GLASS', they would see (according to the Catalogue, itself monumental in three volumes with the details of the glass exhibits beginning on page 699) 'elsewhere . . . various large (glass) objects arranged . . . the size of which will not fail to render them appreciable to the visitor. . . . The great specimens of plate glass, one of which exceeds considerably the size of any previous sheet of glass made in any country . . . suspended from the girders of the roof are costly chandeliers of great magnificence of appearance . . . the Great Crystal Fountain is twenty-seven feet in perpendicular altitude and contains almost four tons of pure Crystal glass.'

Those whose local patriotism drove their tired steps on into the Central North Gallery discovered that magnificence could be expressed in more ways than in staggering size; there, exhibits 14 to 17 showed them magnificence ('subdued grandeur') in design, in colour, in ornament and decoration; the exhibitors were three manufacturers, the Richardsons of Wordsley, Davis, Greathead and Green of Brettell Lane and Thomas Webb of the Platts,

[1] 'Seventeen acres of roofing glass and 1,500 vertical glazed sashes'; four thousand tons of iron.

(a)

PLATE 62.   (a) Witch Bowl.   (b) Bowl.

By courtesy of Webb Corbett Ltd.

(b)

By courtesy of Webb Corbett Ltd.

PLATE 63.   A wine service.

Amblecote, and one engraver, Thomas Wood.[1] The Webbs seem not yet to have aimed at entrance into the 'higher regions of taste'; that was to come later when Thomas Webb's son received the Legion of Honour and his firm, then transferred to a rebuilt Dennis, the only Grand Prix awarded for glass at the Paris Exhibition of 1878; here Thomas Webb was content to show 'various patterns of glass' of which, all table utility ware, the catalogue names thirty and includes others in an '&c.' The glass exhibited by the other two firms was a mixture of that opulent and fantastic glass which was exploited here for another fifty years and glass of a design and treatment which could offend no taste of any period; the workmanship in both was of the highest quality.

There was 'white-glass' (the catalogue's 'flint-glass') in plenty, cut and engraved, gilt and frosted; a Birmingham newspaper claimed that 'the purity of Richardsons' flint has no equal in the exhibition'; but that pre-eminence was challenged by the new coloured glasses. The removal of 'the stringent regulations considered to be necessary to enforce the due observance of the Excise laws' six years previously had opened the gate wide to experiment. It had never been tightly closed; some manufacturers had obviously been friggering as busily in their mixing-rooms as their gaffers did at odd times in the glass-house, for new products, especially coloured glasses, had squeezed through; Thomas Hawkes & Company had brought the 'gold enamel service to perfection' by 1834. It is significant that it was from this Dudley firm that both the Richardsons and William Greathead of Davis, Greathead and Green had come. Before the Great Exhibition the Wordsley firm had introduced 'Chrysolite and topaz' and their glass had been awarded a gold medal by the Royal Society of Arts (1847), but it was Davis, Greathead and Green who showed on the 'cut black flint glass slabs' of their stands the greater variety of new colours: 'ruby, oriental blue, chrysoprase, turquoise, rose colour, opal coated blue, cornelian, opal frosted, pearl opal, mazareen blue &c.'

The 'cased' or 'coated' glass vessels attracted a great deal of admiring attention and W.C.A., in a note on their production in the Catalogue, wrote as blandly of it as the tourist of 1777 had of the enamel twists: 'The manipulation is extremely simple.' He proceeds briefly to describe one of the two methods used by the

[1] Wood is catalogued as 'of Stourbridge'; this gives no clue to the whereabouts of his works; the first two manufacturers are also placed in Stourbridge and Thomas Webb 'near Stourbridge'.

gaffers here, the 'cupping' method. In this a ball of colourless glass was placed inside the waiting cup already fashioned from a stick of the coloured metal; the two were then heated together and treated as a single vessel. The second method was by 'gathering'; the ball of colourless glass gathered the coloured from a dandy pot. Casing was always, and still is, what the local gaffers call a 'caselty' job; unless there is an exact coincidence of coefficients in the two metals, the casing will split and fall away on cooling. Both those famous ancient vases, the Portland and Naples, were cased glasses and when, in the early eighteen-seventies, Philip Pargeter of the Red House Glass Works, Wordsley, commissioned John Northwood to reproduce the Portland Vase, his workmen found it a most difficult problem to supply Northwood with the necessary blank; only at the seventh attempt did they succeed.

Gaffers, cutters, engravers, decorators, all had been called upon to produce work in those new styles which were to remain fashionable for the next half century, Venetian, Egyptian, Etruscan, Grecian, 'after the antique'. But cutting, engraving, gilding, frosting had to surrender pride of place in decoration to the new enamel colours in which, on the many opal jars and vases, were depicted subjects from Aesop's *Fables* or Greek myths, Italian landscapes, marine views, Scotch lochs, pet fawns or Grecian figures.

Davis, Greathead and Green rounded off their exhibit with an educational item: 'specimens of the raw materials from which the articles were produced', so that the visitors could learn and wonder with young James Howell at the 'rare kind of knowledge and chymystry which could transmute Dust and Sand to such diaphanous pellucid dainty bodies' as their exhibits were and, when the firm assured them that 'the whole of the labour and ornamentations were performed by English workmen', they must have been proud indeed of the gaffers of Brettell Lane.

Exhibit 14, that of the Richardsons, was awarded a Prize Medal, 'one Prize Medal only', as 'Captain Owen, R.E., for the Royal Commission for the Exhibition' replied to an enquiry from 'B. Richardson, Esq.'; it was a single as well as a signal honour and there were three partners at a loss how to share it; however, at a cost of one pound each, two duplicates were struck by the Mint and the firm's fraternal framework was not disturbed. One other award came into the district, a diploma to the Amblecote pot-maker, Charles Squires.

The middle years of the century were an uneasy period in the industry; the gaffers and their chairs, the decorators in their shops

PLATE 64. Portland Vase. The first reproduction
by John Northwood the First.

PLATE 65.   Portland Vase.   The first reproduction
by John Northwood the First.

pursued their even way among the opulent and flowery fancies demanded by the public, but in office and board-room there was much shuffling and reshuffling of partners, many transfers from one house to another while gradually that pattern of production was set up which remains to-day. The Webbs were wandering in search of a settled home; a Stevens travelled from Dudley (part of a general trek of the trade from that town) via Coalbournbrook to Moor Lane; the Grazebrooks and the Littlewoods left the industry and the Stuarts came in; the Walkers took over the Heath from the literally bankrupt Ruffords; Davis, Greathead and Green bought the Dial, and for a time ran both that and the Brettell Lane house and then abandoned both.

The brilliance of the Davis, Greathead and Green glass petered out fitfully after its Exhibition triumph, none the less real because it received no official award, and it was the Richardsons, blessed with two medals and a Royal order, who took the lead and held it by their exploitation of new decorative processes and their intro-duction of newer ones. Of the three brother partners, the 'in-genious gentleman' Benjamin was the technical pioneer. As manager of Hawkes and Company of Dudley, he had been par-ticularly interested in etching on glass; at Wordsley he succeeded in devising methods of using this decorative technique, hitherto confined to flat surfaces, on table-wares. Then on his opal and crystal he rang the decoration changes on etching, cutting, enamel-ling and gilding, using these singly or in combinations of any two or sometimes three; items on his price-lists, pitcher-shaped jugs, goblets, finger-bowls and coolers, are described as 'Etched and Gilt on Crystal', 'Enamel on Crystal', 'Enamel on Opal', 'Gold on Opal', 'Gilt on Crystal'; his jug-handles were variously treated, solid, twisted or chain, most bore gold motives; one, a quart size, priced at a guinea, was 'Gold on Crystal with Chain handle solid Gold'. The stems of the goblets of various styles were cut, starred with gold or carried the stems of the marsh-marigold leaf of the bowl-pattern in a twist down to a domed foot which was often folded and always gilt-rimmed.

These were special items which do not appear on the list of 'Nett Prices of Flint Glass' issued on behalf of the Flint Glass Manufacturers; as were also the table-wares on which the glass-cutters exploited their technique to the full. 'Every requisite for the Dinner Table', decanters, jugs, spirit bottles, soda goblets and tumblers, goblets, champagnes, clarets, wines, sugar-bowls, butter-stands, confectioners, jellies, custards, mustards, cruets, pickles, castors, finger-bowls and butter-floats; all these were produced in glass 'from the richest to the commonest quality'; it was presumably the 'Diamond Glass' which led in quality, for 'in sharpness and brilliancy it surpasses the best examples of Old Venetian Glass'. The 'Diamond' label came from the type of cutting not from the surpassing brilliance; glass could not have been cut more intensively; practically every item of the service bristled all over its surface, only the finest of wines could have compensated for the discomfort of their prickly rims. The 'Mediaeval Glass' service was treated with comparative austerity. Two other services challenged the appeal of these to the Richardson customers: one 'Richly Cut in Elliptical Forms with Cut Gothic Scollops', the other 'Richly Cut in deep prisms and having a brilliant and pleasing effect'.

Cut-glass wares are first listed as an addition to the 1844 issue: 'Wines Best Princes and Cobourgs, common fluted not exceeding 4 oz. 4s. 9d. per dozen'; eight-ounce goblets similarly treated were eight shillings the dozen.

The 1850 Price List gives no fewer than 278 items; a comparison of this post-Excise list with that of 1839, six years before the removal of the duties, reveals two facts of interest: the items on both are identical except that the early list contains 'daffys' not included in 1850, and the later list has 'Deck lights' and 'Globes' not shown in 1839, and few of the items show any reduction in price despite the absence of duties; there is one curious exception: among the 'Inks' in 1850 appears the 'Exciseman' which has fallen in price from six shillings to five! At the foot of the later list appears this adjustment, 'Opal Colour Articles 3s. per dozen or 1s. 9d. per lb. extra' and this important new item, 'Pressed Tumblers, 5d. per lb.' The American process of press-moulding was another of the new processes introduced by Benjamin Richardson.

While the Richardsons were thus firmly established, the Webbs' restless wanderings in search of a settled site were only to end when Thomas Webb built a new glass-house on the site of the old Fimbrell House at Dennis. Entering the industry in 1833 by taking over Richard Bradley's original house at Wordsley, he had engaged the two Richardsons, Benjamin and William H. By 1838 the Richardsons (three now by the addition of brother Jonathan) were in possession and Thomas Webb was at the White House as 'Webb and Shepherd' and also at the Platts alone.[1] Soon afterwards Edward and Joseph Webb took over the old Holloway End house from the Littlewoods (ending their forty years' tenure as 'Littlewood and Berry') but by 1850 they had parted company, Edward having taken over the White House and Joseph the second Coalbournbrook house. It was the White House venture which proved the more stable, despite the divided interests of Edward's sons, who were millers and seedsmen as well as glassmen and one of them a Member of Parliament;[2] not stable enough, however; for a time the neighbour Richardsons were in occupation; then at the beginning of this century the Webbs were back again as 'Webb and Corbett'; the new firm's stay lasted a short dozen years at the end of which it took over the Coalbournbrook house abandoned by Joseph Stevens' Executors, where it thrives to-day not many yards distant from Thomas Webb's Dennis.

The entry of the Stuarts as partners in 'Mills Webb and Stuart' was the successful culmination of ambitious years of work in the industry by Frederick Stuart, who had come into it as an eleven-year-old office boy for Richard Bradley Ensell in 1827. His was the only new name of the three; 'Webb' was ubiquitous at the time; 'Mills' had been connected with the Honeybornes at Moor Lane and was in the 'Boulton and Mills' who took over the Audnam Glass-house when the Grazebrooks abandoned glass for iron. Their works, standing within the shadows of Richard Bradley's great cone, they called the Albert Glassworks, presumably in tribute to the Prince Consort, then earnestly trying to persuade not only the English people but also their Queen and his into just appreciation of English industrial achievement.

When the Honeybornes, after running the Moor Lane house for a short time with Joseph Batson in the earliest years of the nineteenth century, handed it over to Silvers and Mills, the last of the old names connected with the industry had gone. The new men had no family craft tradition behind them but, settling into the old houses rich in crystal story, they were inspired by the *genius loci* of a district steeped in two hundred and fifty years' intensive practice of the trade they had adopted and were destined to add fresh leaves to its laurels. Joseph Silvers had come from one

[1] To-day the Webbs and Richardsons are again in close association: 'Thomas Webb and Company' and 'Henry G. Richardson & Sons' both on the Dennis site.

[2] Not the first glassman M.P.; Thomas Hawkes was a Member for Dudley from 1834 to 1844.

of the Coalbournbrook houses; by the time of the Great Exhibition, his two sons-in-law had succeeded him as 'Stevens and Williams'.

The glass-makers had their trade union, 'The National Flint Glass Makers' Friendly Society of Great Britain and Ireland' which had held its first conference at Manchester in 1849; its assets in 1852 were, according to its secretary, 'not fourteen pence' but by 1853 they had risen to fourteen hundred pounds. This phenomenal strengthening of its financial position did not hide the fact that 'Stourbridge, Wordsley and Dudley have nearly three hundred black rats'; here, too, 1854 saw an improvement: 'Since the last reports Stourbridge and Wordsley have increased double in numbers, there are now 32 members.' The glass-cutters also had their Society, 'The United Flint Glass Cutters of Great Britain and Ireland' and their quota of non-Society workers.

By 1858 the 'Friendly Society' was supporting its members in a very unfriendly attack on their employers; from Audnam, on 16 October of that year, the Grazebrooks were writing to the other manufacturers:

'The following men having formed a Combination to stop our Glass Works, and dictate their own rules, have all been discharged by us; and we should be obliged by your not employing them, and feel sure it is the interest of the Glass Trade to support us. Our Glass Cutters are all men unconnected with the Union, and we mean to adopt the same course with the Glass Makers.'

Ten days later, Stevens and Williams from Brierley Hill Glass Works announced that

'In consequence of our refusal to submit to the dictation of the Glass Makers in our employ, the undermentioned have signified their intention of not recommencing work until we comply with their demands . . .'

and, like the Grazebrooks, that they would be obliged

'by your not employing them. . . .'

How hopefully they made that request is uncertain for there were black rats even among the manufacturers; their Association, which called itself 'The Flint Glass Trade' covered the United Kingdom, and in 1839 had forty-five members in England (nine in the Stourbridge district) and four each in Scotland and Ireland. Its meetings seem to have been held as occasion demanded at Newcastle upon Tyne, Crewe, Derby or Birmingham. The agenda was invariably short, its items confined to the purely economic, a necessary rise in prices, an imperative reduction in wages, liability for breakages, payments for carriage and so on; regrettably often, reports were presented of unsocial practices by members, occasionally the delinquent firms were named. If the agenda was short, the journey was often too long for representatives of some firms to attend but the majority of these wrote 'concurring in the objects of the Meeting'. At one meeting at the Union Hotel, Birmingham, in the eighteen-fifties, fifteen firms were represented, six from the Stourbridge district, twenty-six (three from Stourbridge) sent letters and 'no letters were received from' six named others. The black rats were usually among these abstainers.

The language of the manufacturers' resolutions was more restrained than that of the workers' Magazine; 'black rats', 'traitors', 'humbugs and bounces' are common epithets used in this journal's tirades against non-Society men; the Flint Glass Trade more gently, as at Birmingham with 'M. Grazebrook, Esq. in the Chair' in 1850

> 'cannot but express its extreme surprise and regret that Messrs. Powell & Sons should have issued a List so materially under the one issued by the Trade generally, with a Circular announcing a considerable reduction in costs . . . this Meeting cannot refrain from expressing its opinion that the course pursued will have the most disastrous consequences.'

The gaffers ragged their black rats; insulted them in the closed confines of the glass-house and assaulted them in the public inn-yards; the Trade 'respectfully requested' five of its members, including Benjamin Richardson, to confer with the 'Dissentients', that is, the Powells, and asked for a 'Subscription to be entered into of £5 each firm to defray necessary Expenses which was responded to by all present', eleven of them.

For years the Trade had been attempting by circular, meeting or deputation, to put an end to this practice of underselling; not all these were officially sponsored. One curious anonymous effort to strengthen the bonds of association sufficiently to prevent members from straying from the fold emanated from this district in 1847. Benjamin Richardson began it by sending out to all manufacturers of flint glass an anonymous 'Lithographic Circular' diagnosing the ills of the body crystal, chief of which was the evil practice of underselling, and asking for a prescription for a remedy; he signed the appeal 'M.D.' and asked for replies to be sent to 'F.G.M.U., Post Office, Gloucester.'

Unanimously those manufacturers who replied confirmed the

widespread and alarming nature of the symptoms; all condemned underselling emphatically but, beyond expressing the conviction (as did 'E. & J. Webb of Hollowayend Glassworks') that 'it is to the Interest of one and all that We should be united', none made any suggestion of suitable action. 'Glass Masters' Meetings have been tried before and the Faithfull have been the dupes of the Faithless', wrote one despondent gentleman and proceeded merely to repeat the very question he had been asked to answer, 'What can prevent our Large Manufacturers with all the advantages they have from underselling the smaller establishments?' 'I have no objection', wrote another, 'to assist in whatever may be considered practicable to effect a cure', but no prescription was forthcoming. A Bristol manufacturer, disdaining 'anonymous communications', simply referred the sender of the circular to 'Michael Grazebrook Esqr Auldnam near Stourbridge . . . with whom you should correspond with (sic) openly and candidly with your real name who would then no doubt give you his sentiments'. Michael Grazebrook had, of course, already received the circular and he had given his sentiments in a letter no more helpful than the others but characteristically forthright:

'Mr. Anonymous M.D.

You must regenerate the present Assumed Master Glass Manufacturers before you can give firmness and wisdom to act in common honesty towards themselves; they are deservedly looked upon by the enlightened Tradesmen of the present day as a compound of every bad matter that ought to be discarded by a respectable Body. I hope you will drench them with a large dose of the Reform Purge for I found mild apperients had no effect upon their shuffling constitutions altho' aided by a Pocket Pill.

Believe me to remain
Your willing Assistant
M. Grazebrook

I think it would be useless trying Ether for they are stupid enough already.'

An official French *Inquiry into the Treaty of Commerce with England* in 1861 reported

'Goblets of common glass are not generally used in England where the poorest families make use only of crystal. . . . English crystal ware is quite as formidable in the small factories as in the great establishments.'

The great establishments were the glass-houses of the member-firms of the Trade; what were the small factories? The *Inquiry* briefly describes the beginning of one:

'A master assembles several hands, sometimes he is his own chief workman. He constructs a furnace . . . the first materials he buys on credit; a few moulds are ordered . . . and thus he makes the crystal in ordinary use with scarcely any other expense than the price of fuel, the first materials and the labour.'

The evidence given by the gaffer to support his case for the limitation of the number of apprentices contained an estimate that there were in the kingdom at the time fifty-six cribs in which a hundred and thirty-six men were at work. These 'cribs' were the small factories whose crystal challenged that of the great establishments. The gaffer reserved comment on them leaving it to his Magazine to state that 'There is not a more degraded race of beings than the cribmen'. The 'black rats' were in the glass-house and near enough to be bludgeoned into Society membership but the cribmen were slaving in contemptible immunity ('wages below standard and longer hours') for gaffers who were their own masters, ambitious men who had (as the manufacturer already quoted had feared would happen) 'broken off from establishments where they are now employed and endeavour to better themselves and bring forward at a cheaper rate an inferior article', or journeymen making a despairing effort to get a chair of their own.

'Glass', in the words of a late seventeenth century tract,

'unlike other Trades who can have what Workmen they will when they will for glassmakers being bread up always to the Fire cannot turn themselves to other things that if they cannot be Imployed in their own Trade in England must be forced unto Foreign parts.'

Some of these redundant craftsmen actually did emigrate to Ireland or Holland, others went no further abroad than to the nearest vacant stable, nailshop, barn or cottage and began work there. Complete craftsmen as they were, they built their furnaces themselves, often fashioned their own pots, mixed their batch, set and reset their pots, stoked their fires and worked not the traditional six-hour shift but as long as any workable metal remained in the pot. The last task of their usually long day was to mix a new batch and leave it to fuse during the night to be worked on the morrow. Their pots were usually the small 'dandy' or 'skittle' pots, in shape like a stumpy gun-barrel, the type of pot used in the glass-house to hold the different coloured metals and set about the flint pot two above and one on each side.

There was a great increase in the number of cribs after the removal of the duties, but many had existed during the Excise period, hidden in out-of-the-way places, unlicensed and so evading payment of the duties, using the most easily procurable and cheapest raw materials with a big proportion of cullet; some used nothing but cullet ('many poor Families keep themselves from the Parish by picking up broken glass of all sorts to sell to the maker'); they produced phials and scent and drug bottles for apothecaries in great quantities. Indeed at one time they cornered the market in these, or so the Flint Glass Manufacturers were complaining in a letter to the Chancellor of the Exchequer in 1835:

> 'They have taken a branch of the trade that used to be considerable with us, bottles for perfumery and we have nothing of that now.'

The crude requirements of bottle-making all played into the cribman's hand; the cheapest, unrefined materials could be used since the colour of the glass did not matter: any sand, loamy or ferruginous, any kind of waste glass, soapmakers' waste, ground bricks or furnace slag. Alkali, an expensive item in the glass-house was, happily for the cribman, not a desirable ingredient of bottle-glass since it made this less resistant to chemical attack. Again, he could ignore with impunity the Excise regulation which forbade the use of window-glass refuse in bottle-making; and almost any substitute for kiln or lehr could provide all the annealing necessary; indeed, if the bottle were big enough to have a kick in it, it could be left to cool in the open air.

The many cribs which grew up in the Stourbridge district when the Excise century ended made the stock bottles and phials, but some specialized in small coloured canes which they supplied to the glass-houses, others in tubing, while a very common product was the lamp-chimney for the domestic oil-lamp. But soon the independent gaffer in his crib was making almost everything he might have made in the castor-hole chair at a ten-pot furnace, except for the larger vessels. The cribs grew in size as well as number: two or three large pots with one or two dandies and a dozen hands replaced the single pot and the gaffer and his boy.

In the eighteen-sixties a Harrop had gone from Wordsley to set up a crib at Bromsgrove and was making coloured fancy glass-ware, the first of a group of cribs to be worked by glass-makers

"APHRODITE"

PLATE 66. 'Aphrodite' plaque.

PLATE 67. The 'Pegasus' or
'Dennis' Vase.
John Northwood
the First.

*By courtesy of the
Society of Glass
Technology.*

from the Stourbridge district in that old nail-making centre and
to be worked by them for the next sixty years. Harrop was followed by Stevens, again from Wordsley, then by Evans of Brettell
Lane, first in a stable then in a sizable glass-house contrived out
of five derelict cottages. Evans employed as many as eighteen
hands and made flint-glass, ruby and coloured, and the type of
'frigger' which a wide popular demand had converted into stock
glassware, fantastically coloured and ornamented pipes, baskets of
fruit, walking-sticks. Other cribs flourished on an equally keen
public taste for cheap ornamental table ware, sugar-bowls, cream
jugs, flower stands, vases, epergnes.

The glass-cutters did not long leave the glass-makers' sole
possession of this Promised Land of thriving cribs unchallenged;
they set up their wheels and treadle lathes in wooden sheds in the
backyards and gardens of their dwelling-houses, an easier task
than the gaffer's furnace-building. The glass-makers' crib and the
cutter's domestic shop usually worked in happy association, the
gaffer supplying the grinder with blanks, plain vessels to be cut
or engraved or both.

While the maker's crib has now almost disappeared, the cutters'
sheds are still busy. One unique crib has been set up since the
Second World War, a crib that is a modern glass-house in
miniature.[1] Fred Harper, fifty-year-old member of a family of
glassmen and a Dennis product, bought an old malt-house in
Amblecote, standing just outside the boundary of Thomas Hill's
Dennis Park. On the ground floor he built his own furnace save
for that dome which demands a bricklayer's specialist skill; he
mixes his own batch, sets his pots and gaffers it *in toto*. A cutting-
shop on the first floor sets the seal of completeness on this modern
crib; there his son decorates the 'beautiful articles for ornament or
use' which he fashions below. His furnace is gas-fired; his pots
are made less than two hundred yards away in Brettell Lane by a
Squire. Squires worked with Henzeys three centuries and a half
ago and Squires have been making glass-house pots in Amblecote
for the last 175 years and, true to Lorrainer tradition, in a father-
son succession.

The glass-maker's tools are simple, efficient and ancient;
Squire's tool is a finer and more ancient one than human ingenuity
ever invented, his own hand. We can date the Squires' association
with English glass from nearly four hundred years ago; as potters,

[1] The incidence of purchase-tax has meant a temporary suspension of work
in this crib.

their methods date from the tool-less days of pre-history. As in those ancient days, the pots are built up layer by layer, shaped dandy-open or dome-roofed for crib or glass-house, smoothed to a finish all and only by a pair of knowing Squire hands; and it is by air and not by fire that they are dried into that structural strength that can withstand the whitest heats of any fuel without and the great weight of molten metal within.

Some of the larger cribs of the late nineteenth century were really glass-houses; the name seems to have been given to any building used for glass-making, whatever its size and the number of pots, which was not originally built for that purpose. Contempt for them and their non-Society workers persisted with members of both Makers' and Cutters' Societies; to them cribs were always black rat-holes; the cone was an honest and honoured symbol of the trade standing on the king's highway, the crib a shabby shanty in hiding because of the degrading practices carried on within, a place in which 'the beautiful trade of Glassmaking is brought as low as nail-making'.

In 1857 the Wordsley Branch of the United Flint Glass Cutters' Society published a placard:

> 'TO ALL WHOM IT MAY CONCERN
> Several parties in Brettell-Lane and Wordsley having adver-
> tized for a number of Boys, from 14 to 16 years of age, under
> the pretence of learning them the art of FLINT GLASS CUTTING
> we the GLASS CUTTERS feel it our duty to inform the Public . . .'

the information conveyed a warning that the non-Society practices of these 'parties' were calculated to produce most ruinous
consequences to the 'Rights of Labour':

> 'The Employers alluded to are Middle Men or Small Masters,
> standing between the Manufacturer & the Workman in our
> Trade more especially in this District; the men have suffered
> most severely from this state of things and we consider it to
> be our bounden duty to put an end to such a ruinous system.'

The Introduction to the Glass Section of the *Official Catalogue
of the Great Exhibition*, on the other hand, had seen cribs merely
as centres of great activity:

> 'The commoner kinds of blown and pressed glass are pro-
> duced in large quantities by persons having only a small
> amount of capital, manufacturing on a limited scale at a cheap
> rate and requiring a rapid conversion of the proceeds of their
> little furnaces into money.'

Omitting the pressed glass and the cheap rate, this definition would have covered all the early glass-houses in the Stourbridge district; they all required this rapid conversion of their products into ready money; they had to be financed out of the family income but the high price of their glass enabled that family to live without stint.

Chapter 12

FORWARD TO THE PRESENT

Throughout the second half of the nineteenth century, the glassmen of the Stourbridge district continued to indulge in that orgy of ornament and decoration which the Great Exhibition had advertised to the world. The beauties of the gaffer's work, his shapes, his cased glasses, his pot-coloured metals in all the new colours which had been creeping into the mixing-rooms from the Continent via London shops and show-rooms, were almost smothered by the additions of the decorators, the painters in enamels, the gilders (and later the silverers), the etchers and engravers.

The painters left Greek shores and classic myth for subjects nearer home, Matlock and Stratford appeared as well as Athens, elegant Victorian ladies elbowed Penelope out, cupids boated on English lakes, shooting scenes ousted Bacchanalian feasts, the pictures being painted on backgrounds of opal, blue or gold. The 'Egyptian, Etruscan and Grecian styles' of Davis, Greathead and Green gave way to one which can only be called Victorian. Colour invaded even the dinner-table, hitherto the preserve of colourless crystal; if the colourmen failed to seize dominion over the service, they lorded it over the table from under a flashing chandelier, where towered and sprawled a table-centre two feet high with fruit-bowl on top and three or four curved-leaf or spiral-twisted crook arms holding hanging baskets with coloured glass pendants and chains hanging from each arm, all standing in a wide shallow bowl with beaded edge or on a mirror base. To challenge that dominion the cutters and engravers and etchers worked at the gaffer's decanters and celery-vases, his pickle-jars and butter-tubs with their Gothic ovals, fans, multiple scallops, flutes, stars, prisms, fruits and flowers and ferns until no space was left on which any one of them could further exploit his cunning.

The English have always been fond of decoration and ornament; they took this coloured glass to their hearts and the manufacturers saw to it that they took it also to their homes. Not far away, the Worcester potters were feeding the same appetite with the same wealth of colour and pattern though they could not compete with the gaffers' shapes. Mantel-pieces, what-nots, dressing-tables were all heavy with it; the gaffers, answering its invitation to play, friggered it into fantastic shapes which they proudly bore before them under their Society banner on their Whitsun parades, to their picnics in Prestwood Park, to Stewponey by canal-boat, by brake to Bewdley.

Let us look at some specimen darlings of the Victorian homes; the descriptions come from catalogues of local collections at Brierley Hill and Stourbridge. Here is a vase:

'White bulbous body, narrow neck with flange mouth and escalloped top, cut pineapple form at base of body and prism flutes to the top. Pomona green alabaster stem and flower-shaped foot with gilt escalloped edge.'

A second:

'Bristol blue glass with gilt panel showing picture of Victorian lady in enamel, background of gilt rosettes.'

A third:

'Shell shape body iridised. Green foot representing seaweed.'

A violet-holder:

'Globular shape, honeycomb moulded body with flanged and crimped top, shaded from blue into yellow, ivy leaf feet.'

A claret glass:

'Blue cased bowl, slender drop stem, blown foot. Etched to crystal leaving blue designs in relief.'

A decanter:

'Antique shape, flint handle, light green body, bubbly aventurine and white splashes.'

These are instructions given to cutters for a 'celery-vase':

'Drop and merese stem Celery Vase as 2846; cut 6 fan scallops with 12 fan cuts under, 6 laced Gothic ovals; fill in with broad laced prisms fingered round and small fans below engrave Flowers round the ovals 7 stem flutes.'

The coloured glass ware was gaffer's work and in some ways as good as gaffer's work could be; too often decoration was simply gilding the lily. Choicest of this ware were the simplest cased glasses, ruby or blue or green over flint with the design cut or etched through the casing to the flint base; even in this the gaffer's skill was exploited; two or more casings, as blue over opal over crystal or opal over ruby over citron, gave the cutter opportunity to vary the colour of his background or provided a coloured frame for panels.

However, amid this crush of coloured ware the dinner service shone mostly crystal clear; the Richardsons were offering seven services, three of them etched with formal, floral decorations in rings of varying depths, and the others cut with fringe, diamond band, diamond and fan or prism and diamond patterns.

The many chandeliers produced here for dining-rooms, for ball and assembly rooms, for English mansions, hotels and guildhalls and for palaces and mosques in the Near (and Further) East were usually white crystal but often coloured; a mosque in Mauritius is 'hung with dozens of magnificent ones flashing with red and blue and crystal drops and filling the place with a thousand coloured fires'.[1] Walkers at the Heath made one for Constantinople which cost the Sultan of Turkey £10,000 and a most handsome one appeared in the Dennis exhibit which won the Grand Prix at Paris in 1878.[2]

The production of utility table ware, like the Richardsons' services, generally over-cut, persisted here through all the years of the century, through all the reaction against cut-glass which came of the criticism of Ruskin and the more practical strictures of William Morris. The gaffers, who had been Ruskinians before he was born, had now come to see that all cutting was not barbarous, that breaking the surface of their glass here and there gave it an added beauty which the unrelieved rounded surface did not possess since its transparency was cloaked by reflection; they objected only when their shapes were distorted. The English people never surrendered to Ruskin's eloquence and applauded all the glass-cutter's extravagances. But that they shared, without knowing it, Ruskin's chief enthusiasm is shown by the frequent appearance of Gothic arches and ovals in the cutter's patterns.

In the last thirty years of the century, it was not the iron and stone wheels of the cutter, however, grind how they might, which carried the glass industry of the Stourbridge district to one of its greatest triumphs, but the smaller, the tiny copper wheels of the engraver and the steel gravers of the glass-sculptors. And it was more than the foot on the treadle that drove those wheels; there was the infinitely patient and skilful art of the craftsmen, English and foreign, there was their loving devotion to their craft, there

---

[1] *Shoals of Capricorn* by F. D. Ommanney.
[2] This chandelier converted to carry ninety candlelights instead of the original thirty-six was awarded a second Grand Prix at the Paris Exhibition of 1889. To-day, wired for thirty-six electric lights, it hangs in the hall of Dennis House, Amblecote, the showrooms and offices of Thomas Webb and Sons.

were the resources in capital and enthusiasm of visionary manufacturers. There was always the trusted gaffer to provide the
foundation.

In Langford's *Staffordshire and Warwickshire, Past and Present*,
it is baldly stated that 'Schinner, a foreign artist, was the first
successful engraver of glass at Stourbridge in 1660'. There is
no evidence to corroborate this; engraving at that time was done
by diamond point; if such a man worked here, then the district
was most fortunate in having a visit from one of the few nomad
engravers from Western Europe. The first record of wheel-
engraving is an advertisement which appeared in 1769 asking for
information about a Wordsley apprentice to the trade who had
absconded from his employers, Pidcock, Ensell and Bradley.

The last three decades of the nineteenth century and the first of
the twentieth cover the great period of engraving and its kindred
art of cameo-carving in the Stourbridge district. Some of its great
names are foreign, Fritsche, Kny, Keller, Lechevrel, Palme,
Kreschmann, Hanke, but Woodall, Northwood, Hodgetts, Locke,
Fereday are English enough; as are those of Richardson, Webb,
Pargeter, Stuart, Stevens and Williams, the manufacturers who
fostered these twin-arts, not only as employers but also as patrons.
Benjamin Richardson with his devotion to the craft and his
inspiring enthusiasm, complete glassman without peer, presided
over the birth of this remarkable period; already he had introduced
press-moulding,[1] etching, gilding and a new method of 'threading' glass[2] and had intensively explored the possibilities of
enamelling. He had attracted gifted youths to apprenticeship, who
became infected with the same fervour of service to the craft and
the same will to cherish it. When Thomas Webb, Philip Pargeter
(a nephew) and John Northwood stepped out of Richardsons' to
their own several triumphs, they went as apostles of the Richardson creed.

The most publicized single achievement of the period was the
reproduction of the Portland Vase by John Northwood. Ever since
it had been discovered that this sepulchral vase was made of glass
and not earthenware or stone, the more technically minded of glass
manufacturers, that is, those who were glassmen and not mere
businessmen, men like Richardson, confident that what the

[1] Joseph Stevens at Coalbournbrook and Joseph Webb at Holloway End
followed Richardson's example and introduced press-moulding in these houses.
[2] The machine with which this threading was done is still to be seen at the
works of Stuart and Sons, Wordsley.

Romans had done their own workmen could do to-day, became pre-occupied with the problem of how to do it and possessed by the intent to get it done. Though in the event it was Philip Pargeter who commissioned John Northwood to do it and supplied him, after much trial and error, with the blank, it was Ben Richardson who had inspired Northwood with the assured belief that the laurels were his for the trying. As early as 1860 the now elderly master was constantly holding the Vase as an ideal before his apprentices' eyes and offering a thousand-pound reward to the one who would produce a copy. Northwood set about preparing himself for the task; it was not a job for the engraver's fixed wheel under which the glass was moved; in cameo-carving the glass had to be still for the tools to work over it. But what were to be the tools? Northwood made his own: gravers of thin steel rods set in wooden handles, their ends ground into a long triangular pyramid, with the constantly sharpened apex of which the glass surface was cut away. The experience of his long years of practice of the craft modified and developed these crude originals, the gravers being later held in brass tubes with adjustable jaws which allowed them to be kept of a constant length; by the time he was at work on the Pegasus Vase for Thomas Webb's son, he was using a sculptor's mallet and chisels. But by that time, 1882, he had long had a decorating shop of his own[1] and had trained apprentices in the revived art. Among these were the Woodall brothers, George and Tom, his own nephews, William and Carl Northwood, and his son John, who were further to develop tools and technique and actually bring the engraver's wheel into their tool-kit.

Philip Pargeter, who had served his apprenticeship with his uncle Richardson, became later a partner with him and one of the Hodgetts family at the Red House, Wordsley, which had been taken over in the early eighteen-thirties by Hodgetts and Davies, one of the Dudley glass firms which trekked from that town to Wordsley and Brettell Lane. In 1869, the partnership was dissolved and Pargeter, who had been manager, remained as 'Manufacturer of Flint and Coloured Glass in great Variety'. While he had been managing the Red House, he had been watching Northwood's progress in glass-carving with an almost proprietary interest. Northwood for some years had been at work in what time he could spare from his decorating business on a two-handled vase, not a cased vessel but of pure crystal, for Sir Benjamin Stone. The carved decoration is wholly Grecian and

[1] In Barnet Lane, Wordsley.

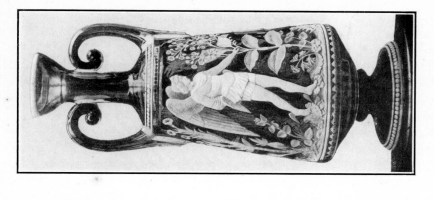

(b) The 'Milton' Vase.
John Northwood the First.

PLATE 68.   (a)   Three Woodall vases.

By courtesy of the Society of Glass Technology.

PLATE 69.

(a) and (b)

*By courtesy of
the Society of
Glass Technology.*

(a) 'Moorish Bathers' plaque by George Woodall.

(b) Cameo carver at work.

formal save for a frieze, half the depth of the body from the shoulder, carved with copies of equestrian groups from the Elgin Marbles. The eight years of carving practice on this 'Elgin Vase' were so successful a proving ground for tool and hand that Pargeter thought the time ripe for the greater task of the Portland Vase. He commissioned Northwood who, with the co-operation of the British Museum authorities, the Pargeter patronage and his own infinitely patient care and skill, completed the work in three years. The patronage continued; another vase, the 'Milton' with figures of Adam and Eve and the Archangel Michael in the Garden of Eden, followed; then three tazzas with a carved head in the centre of each, Literature, Science and Art being represented by Shakespeare, Newton and Flaxman; the first two of these would choose themselves; Flaxman of all the great artists was a peculiarly apposite and happy choice.

Northwood found another patron in Thomas Webb's son, Thomas Wilkes Webb, who commissioned what came to be known as the 'Dennis' or 'Pegasus' vase. It was the pioneer's last work and, if not the finest, is probably the largest cameo vase ever made; the Portland Vase stands some nine and a half inches high, the Pegasus twenty-one inches. Venus and her attendants and Aurora with hers adorn the body of the vase; Pegasus appears in the handles and the lid, all three carved from solid opal glass; each handle is the head and neck while the lid is the whole winged body of the fabulous flying horse.

For the Richardsons, Joseph Locke showed that Northwood's reproduction of the Portland Vase was not a unique achievement by producing a second copy and the Frenchman, Alphonse Lechevrel, followed with some fine vases with Grecian subjects. For the Webbs at Dennis, a Bohemian engraver, Frederick Kny, in his Platts workshop produced an 'Elgin' claret-jug; round both body and stopper of this run friezes of Greek horsemen, while footmen march around the neck. This piece, on which Kny's wheel had challenged Northwood's gravers in the 'Elgin' vase, was part of the successful Dennis exhibit at the Paris Exhibition of 1878.[1]

While the masters were winning such victories for the industry in a new field, their apprentices were fitting themselves for further

[1] H. J. Powell in his *Principles of Glassmaking*, 1883, writes: 'In the Paris Exhibition of 1878 in the British section were some vases carved by hand labour, the actual carving of excessive [sic] delicacy . . .'

In the Stourbridge Collection is a claret-jug on which William Fritsche also used this 'Elgin' motif.

triumphs. George Woodall, who was to become most famous of the group of cameo-workers (and probably the most prolific) with his brother Tom, after serving apprenticeships at the Northwood decorating shop, moved to Dennis. There in a Webb workshop they worked for a time in conjunction and jointly signed their pieces. The brothers were fortunate in the guidance of their uncle Thomas Bott, who was working for some time as a decorator for the Richardsons; he was already well-known for his work on porcelain (Worcester) and there is more than a suggestion of the fleshly female figures he painted on Limoges enamel, white on a dark blue ground, in his nephew George's subjects. Under Bott's influence George Woodall attended the Art School and visited various schools on the continent. At Dennis, the brothers at first used only the Northwood hand tools, but gradually introduced the use of the engraver's wheel, which enabled the always lengthy process to be speeded up. A quarrel broke this fraternal partnership and George continued alone. Soon he began to introduce backgrounds to his figures; his wealth of detail in these and the extreme delicacy of his distance effects are equally astonishing; these are well illustrated in his plaque, 'Moorish Bathers'. A Dennis colleague of Woodall's, the Irishman O'Fallon, was particularly happy in his choice of fruits and flowers as subjects.

In this the Irishman had a very accomplished competitor in the Black Country man, Joshua Hodgetts, who at the Northwood shop worked chiefly for Stevens and Williams. There was nothing stylized about Joshua's flowers; nature was good enough for him and he was naturalist as well as craftsman who would correct the design provided by reference to the actual flower or leaf set up on his bench.

This truth to Nature was typical of the Northwood shop, where, in addition to the Northwoods, father, son and nephews, men like Hodgetts, W. Bowen and James Hill were only the best known of a team of craftsmen skilled in engraving as well as cameo work.[1] At Dennis, the Woodalls had a similar team and the same association of engraver, designer and carver.

The work of the cameo-carvers was more spectacular than that of their colleagues, the engravers pure and simple (the cameo men had latterly been sculptor-engravers) but these, in addition to

[1] Decorative work for Stevens and Williams during this period was done by a number of outside shops; a typical page from their pattern and price book gives the names of Northwood (engraved crests and monograms), Tom Wood (formal floral engraved designs) and Schiller.

their work-a-day formal and floral borders and fillings, some of this work approaching diamond-point delicacy, produced pieces, vases, decanters, claret-jugs, bowls and baskets, which were superb in workmanship if not in design and achieved an astonishing likeness to that Rock Crystal after which their kind was named. Frederick Kny and his team (here again including other Knys, his sons) produced outstanding work in this genre, father Frederick's vases 'Hunting the Eagle' and 'The Waterfall'[1] setting their own high standards. And at Dennis William Fritsche, host of the 'Red Lion' in Brettell Lane as well as master engraver, adorned the Webb gaffers' shapes with work of such quality that glassmen of to-day still speak of it and him with something approaching awe.

Much, probably the greater part, of this work in cameo, Rock Crystal and the misnamed 'crystal-cameo', was bought by American dealers. Then the demand died with the century. Two types of imitation cameo were being exploited; in one the redundant opal was eaten away by acid leaving a thin flat design on the flint; in the other a cameo design was painted in enamel on the vessel and this was then fired. However, some of the more devoted carvers could not abandon the craft. George Woodall carved on and carried his plaques on fine linen to a trusted workman to remove with his wooden discs even the slightest scratch on the back of them. Retiring from Dennis in 1910 he worked until shortly before his death in 1925 in his own workshop at his Kingswinford home. Two of the Northwoods, the son John and the nephew Will Northwood, also still cherished the art and both produced plaques carved only by the hand tools of the first John without the aid of the engraver's wheel. There is a market for cameo work to-day, but the demand is the antique dealer's for pieces of this period and products of these shops, not for a second revival of the ancient craft.

Two features of the development of the glass industry in the Stourbridge district in the second half of the nineteenth century were specially noted by writers: first, the fall from public favour of glass-cutting and the rise into its place of engraving and second, the concentration of the industry in the hands of a few large manufacturers. Certainly, glass-cutting retired for a time into the shadows but it soon climbed back to that throne which it still occupies; the cribs meanwhile guaranteeing that no rust gathered on the practice by turning out over-cut wine suites and table-ware for the still faithful.

[1] Now in possession of his son, Mr. F. Kny of Amblecote.

On the business side, the concentration of the industry continued and the lines of to-day's pattern were firmly drawn. Many of the crowd of cribs which had sprung up like mushrooms, like mushrooms faded; some of the older glass-houses finally closed down; the movement of Dudley glass manufacturers into new partnerships in old Wordsley houses went on; the coming of the bottle-making machine put out the fires in the bottle-houses. The glass-making area contracted into a narrow strip lying along the Stourbridge–Wolverhampton road, scarcely a mile in length and not many yards in width, its limits being Coalbournbrook in Amblecote and the canal at Wordsley; outside that strip stood one solitary but famous house, Stevens and Williams, still in Moor Lane but on a new site. Two new firms began operations in the first quarter of the twentieth century, new only in that they were separate, within those same narrow limits; they were cuttings from old plants rather than new seedlings.

The old 'great glasshouse' of Thomas Hamond on Jeremy Bague's ground and Wheeley's, after its brilliant Davis, Greathead and Green chapter, both in Brettell, had gone; the Heath house let out its last fires in 1882. Their story is summarized in the old gaffer's dictum that 'You can make money in glass like turning a tap on and lose it just as fast.' Holloway End was kept falteringly alive by various owners on various products, the sad end of this famous old house under the Flemings illustrates pointedly the dependence of a house on its workmen; a broken machine is easily replaced; when Flemings with orders in hand for those wine suites for which they were noted failed to get a first-class wine servitor only because no such man was available, the flag of surrender was hoisted; most of the men of Flemings' 'shops', as local glassmen had taken to call their chairs, went to one of the new firms. Coalbournbrook, now only one house, went through phases of desertion and experimental tenure until Webb and Corbett again stabilized it when they transferred from the White House in 1914. For a few years at the end of the nineteenth century the 'British Lens and Wall Glazing Company', emulating the Chances, had produced lenses there and, anticipating Pilkingtons, was one of the first firms to exploit the opportunities which architecture was beginning to offer the industry with its 'opal wall-glazing tiles'.

The old Dial suffered empty years and fitful reoccupations; last home of that window-glass which had been the first product of the local industry, it finally abandoned this for bottles; through its unsettled years its output varied between these and cut table glass. Then a new Dial was built nearer the Stour and the old Henzey foundation was demolished. Of late years it has regained its pre-eminence but in another and new field; to-day Plowden and Thompson's new Dial is one of the largest makers of glass-tubing and rod in the country.

John Pidcock's Platts Bottle-House also had its vicissitudes. But it was there that Thomas Webb laid the foundations for his later Dennis triumphs in a short tenure during which he produced glass fit for the world's eye at the Great Exhibition. At the beginning of the new century a Phoenix Glass Company put the Platts in the charge of one of the best-known and most skilful of gaffers, Tom Jukes, who in a crib standing in the shadow of the Holloway End house had been producing wonderfully coloured and fashioned ware, particularly those many-branched flower-stands with their trumpet vases (the gaffers called them 'carrots') which were best-sellers. Jukes was a uniquely complete craftsman: competent in all the cribman's skills, pot-making, pot-setting, batch-mixing for plain or coloured ware, in fashioning whatever shape he or his customer fancied, in colour experiment; he was first in the district to introduce copper-ruby for the usual pot-ruby obtained by the use of gold.[1] Blower, founder, potmaker, he was also his own smith, able to make any tool he required. The workman of to-day has the utmost difficulty in obtaining new tools and in getting old ones repaired, the old glass-house smiths have disappeared; Tom Jukes needed no smith's help, not even for that most difficult of tasks, making a gadget; he could make his own as he could also that one among all his moulds which produced the crimped edge. When during the first World War the firm was making ship lights he invented a machine which cut the blown glass into the required sections. It was to the Platts under the new Harbridge firm which followed Jukes that Flemings' men came from Holloway End. The 'Harbridge' venture (Harvey and Bridgens, both of the Bridgens glassmaking family) after a rather hazardous launching has enjoyed a prosperous voyage. At first producing blanks for such decorating firms as Hingley's of Wordsley, it soon set up its own shop, Joe Harrop, Dennis-trained and with a thriving cutter's crib at Wordsley, coming in to take charge.

Nobody took over the old Audnam Bank house when Boulton and Mills after seventy-two years abandoned it; in 1928 it was

[1] Cribmen used to buy old pots from the glass-houses to recover for their own use such gold as was left in them.

demolished. But before this, a new Audnam house had been set up, like the new Dial nearer the Stour. Here again, workmen (and staff) from one of the old houses, Dennis, provided the nucleus of trained 'shops' on which the new venture was founded, the Stour-bridge Glass Company.

So time determined the pattern of the 'Stourbridge Glass' industry of to-day in such a way that through every house runs the stream of the three hundred and fifty-year-old tradition.

The industry had suffered more than one crisis in its long life before the first half of the twentieth century plunged it into troubles of a new kind and difficulties with some of which it still struggles. There were the economic stringencies of the War Tax years, 1695–9, and the technical hindrances of the Excise century, 1745–1845, both much exaggerated in manufacturers' reports; there was the victory of crown-glass over that broad which was the staple product of the district, which might have proved fatal to the industry's existence but for the foresight of Thomas Henzey. With the new century, however, came a very definite change for the worse in the economic climate, caused chiefly by the competition of cheap continental glassware on an unprotected home market; again the effects of this were much amplified by political propaganda for it became a party issue, the parties being then Free Traders and Protectionists rather than Liberals and Tories. But while in the War Tax and Excise periods fortunes were being made in glass, in the nineteen-hundreds we find such significant happenings as the sacking of the gardener at Dennis on grounds of economy.

The two World Wars imposed the same kind of conditions on the industry, differing only in degree, restrictions on normal production during the second being as much harsher as national necessity was greater. The small amount of table-ware produced by government permission was for Service departments; a smaller output of cheap tumblers only partially replaced domestic wastage. Decorating shops were closed, the workmen, except for a few grinders retained for puntying, being directed into other trades, from which many were destined never to return to the frame; in the glass-houses chairs were broken up and electric light bulbs, radio and radar equipment, tubing, valves and all kinds of scientific apparatus displaced the domestic and fancy wares.

In the inter-war years cheap foreign imports were still depressing the industry and hindering expansion; these imports more than doubled themselves in weight between the years 1921 and

1930 and became progressively cheaper still, an 103 per cent increase in quantity showing one of only 47 per cent in value. During the slump of 1931–2 protective duties, clamoured for over a long period by the manufacturers, were imposed by the government on foreign ware; these ensured a much greater share of the home market to the home industry.

But no duty or subsidy, indeed no financial measure whatever could solve what had become (and still remains) the industry's greatest problem, the supply of trained workmen; the provision of new gaffers as the old ones (always regretfully) leave their chairs or are taken from them by disablement or death. There are gaffers still being kept on at work to-day well into their seventies, some as gaffers still, some in lower grades of the chair's hierarchy, doing a 'big lad's job', that is, taking-in. One chief cause of this shortage of competent craftsmen has been the gradual raising of the school-leaving age; one school-year after another has been added until to-day's fifteen years is, in every gaffer's estimation, an age too late to begin the necessary training. The great gaffers of old and those whom age is now forcing into retirement entered the glass-house at any time from their ninth to twelfth years; by their sixteenth year they had become intimate with every process, with the very stuff of glass; such initiation ensured that they were glassmen for life. To-day's boy has not reached that stage when he is whisked away to his national service and rarely returns to resume his training.

The skills required in such glass-making as is practised in the Stourbridge district, that is, in hand-blown work, are all the more difficult of attainment than in other handicrafts as the medium is more ductile, more insistent on the seizing of the quickly passing, only possible moment for the application of those skills. The mastery of the gaffer is not for all who practise the craft; the proficiency which is all that most can attain demands a longer period of training than competence in any other craft. The confident self-possession, the exact co-ordination of expert hand with intuitive eye are the products of many longer years than modern conditions offer the aspirant of to-day. And of these aspirants there are fewer every year.

In their struggle against the competition of cheap foreign glass, the manufacturers of Stourbridge glass did not leave everything to the Government; laying aside their traditional designs, both in shape and decoration, for a time they attempted to take the public fancy with new designs by new designers and these designers they

149

engaged from outside the trade, architects, painters, that is, artists who were not glassmen. But between the manufacturer and the public there is always the retailer; the new 'contemporary' designs failed to tempt that middleman. The public he cherished wanted 'cut crystal' and the new designers offered 'cut crystal' but the two laid emphasis on only one, and that different, of the two words, the public on 'cut' and the artist on 'crystal'. The artist, knowing enough of glass, despite his being an outsider, to recognize that the traditional decorative patterns in exploiting one beauty of glass had hidden the others, produced pieces that gave the gaffer's glass opportunity to show all its beauties, shape, texture, colour, brilliancy; to the public only the last mattered, to please it the vessel must blaze all over, in sunlight, firelight, candlelight, there must be rainbows on every square inch of its surface; where the Victorians had revelled in colour, the Edwardians and Georgians gloried in glitter.

What Keith Murray designed for Stevens and Williams, Graham Sutherland, Eric Ravilious and Laura Knight for Stuarts failed to take the retailer's fancy, fine as their work was, especially Murray's; his designs showed an awareness of glass, an approach to that intimacy with it which is so essential, which was surprising in an outsider.

The successful designer of glassware must be a glassman, brought up in the trade; a long acquaintance is as necessary to him as to the gaffer, and designer and gaffer should be as intimate with each other as each with glass. The old gaffers seem to have known this. At the head of the Certificate of Membership of the 'Flint Glass Makers' Friendly Society' in 1874 (of a size and handsomeness, twenty-seven inches by twenty-four and in colour, which proclaimed the gaffer's pride in his craft) stands a symbolic group. The artist and glass-maker kneel opposite each other, the artist surrounded by his papers, brushes, palette and paints, the gaffer among his tools and shapes; their right hands are clasped, their left hands hold, one his design, the other his wine-glass. Standing behind and above them, the appropriate Muse holds identical laurel wreaths above their almost identical heads. The only difference in the appearance of the two men is that the artist wears a coat while the gaffer is in his shirt sleeves. Above the Muse, hovering in bright rays of sunshine, is a dove bearing the olive twig.[1] In 1874 the retailer did not seem to matter; nor could

[1] This symbolic group, suggested by Ben Richardson, was used also by the Glasscutters' Society for their membership card.

any gaffer, designer or manufacturer then foresee that the glass-making they practised in the Stourbridge district was fated to become not a universal provider but a luxury trade. The machine which was to produce 'beautiful articles of use or ornament' was still half a century ahead.

That machine has not yet come to the Stourbridge district, but the shops here are full of its products, articles of use, beautiful enough in some cases to remain as ornaments when use is satisfied. No handicraft could compete with the machine's ability to turn out what the public wants in the quantities it requires at the price it is able and willing to pay. This fact has decided the future of the glass industry of the Stourbridge district; it can now serve only a cultivated taste and the market of a sophisticated minority in England and that minority will remain a minority despite a steady growth of aesthetic appreciation fostered by exhibitions, radio programmes and library facilities. If the purses of this minority kept growing pace with that appreciation hopes would be brighter.

The financially restricted demand of this home group is at present, as far as volume of trade is considered, largely compensated for by the freer and larger purses of a less sophisticated public in the Americas; there the public demands decoration of a type its own factories fail to provide and in which the glass-houses here excel, especially cutting; its fancy for the traditional English patterns tends to confirm the conservative tastes of our manufacturers at the same time as the more critical demands at home encourage experiment in design and decoration. But above the glass-houses in Amblecote, Wordsley and Brierley Hill, still after three hundred and fifty years at work to a happily balanced programme in which pioneering endeavour springs from the firm ground of that long tradition, hovers the threat of slow extinction. It is on the gaffer that the whole industry depends and the gaffer is dying out.

APPENDIX I
THE HENZEY DYNASTY

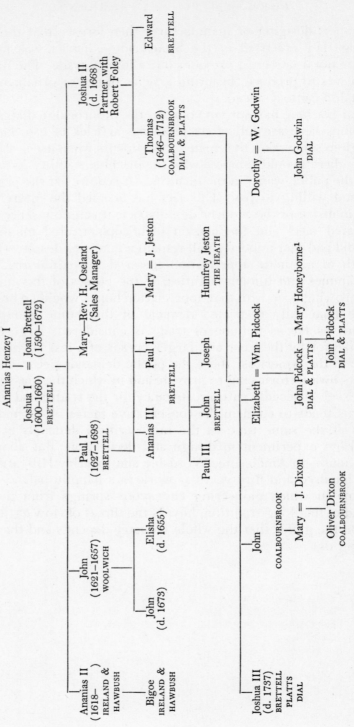

Ananias Henzey I

Joshua I = Joan Brettell
(1600–1660)   (1590–1672)
BRETTELL

¹ Mary Honeyborne was grand-daughter and heiress of Thomas Hamond of BAGUE's; John Pidcock was heir to Joshua III.

The above table contains the names of those Henzeys only who took an active part in the industry; the names in capitals are those of the glass-houses they worked.

APPENDIX II

SUMMARY OF SIGNIFICANT DATES

c. 1610. 'There was Glasse made with Coale upon my ground by native Glasse-makers.' Lord Dudley's claim in 1624.

1611. Oldwinsford Court Leet's ordinance against burning of bracken.

1612. Son of Paul Tyzack baptized at St. Mary's, Kingswinford.

1616. 'Paul Tyzack. gent' landowner in Oldswinford.   COLEMANS.

1618. Joshua Henzey I marries Joan Brettell.
Du Houx and Daniel Tittery at work here.   HOLLOWAY END.

1630. Joshua Henzey landowner in Brettell.   BRETTELL.

1644. Julius Caesar Rackett (Rachetti of l'Altare) working here.

c. 1645. Jeremiah Bague builds glasshouse in Brettell.   BAGUE'S.

1649. Ananias Henzey I buys land for glasshouse in Brettell.   HAWBUSH.

c. 1650. Thomas Rogers (son-in-law to Daniel Tittery) at Holloway End.

1653. John Henzey (Joshua's second son) Customary Tenant of Kingswinford Manor—an English gentleman.
The Visitalias, Abraham, Jacob and Benjamin, working here.

1660. Joshua Henzey I dies. Third son, Paul I, takes over; older brothers, Ananias in Ireland, John working the Woolwich house; Joshua II in partnership with Robert Foley, sole merchants for district's broad-glass.
Colemans chair working temporarily for Foley at Chelwood.

1670 to 1685. Onesiphorus and Jeremiah Dagnia working here.

c. 1670. Edward Bradley builds glasshouse at Audnam.   AUDNAM.

c. 1680. Thomas Bradley builds Fimbrell Glasshouse.   DENNIS.

c. 1690. The Jestons at the Heath.   THE HEATH.
The Littles of Amblecote making glass at Bristol.

1691. The Batchelors take over Dennis.

1692. Thomas Henzey (son of Joshua II) buys Harlestones.   COALBOURNBROOK.

1703. The Perrotts of Bristol sign Broad-Glass Cartel Agreement with the Henzeys, Tyzacks and Batchelors.

1704. Thomas Henzey builds the Dial and shortly afterwards the Platts Glasshouses. THE DIAL. PLATTS.

c. 1710. Winsor James at Dob Hill glasshouse, Wordsley. DOB HILL.

1712. Thomas Henzey dies; son Joshua III succeeds.

1720. The Batchelors making crown glass at Dennis.

1732. Robert Honeyborne buys land at Moor Lane.

1737. Joshua III, last of the Henzeys, dies; nephew John Pidcock succeeds.

1747. Michael Grazebrook takes over Audnam Glasshouse.

c. 1750. 'A manufacture of china' reported in the district. Richard Bradley builds his first glasshouse at Wordsley. BRADLEY'S.

1751. Dr. Pococke reports Stourbridge as being especially famous for coloured glass. MOOR LANE.

1760. First record of cut-glass chandeliers being made here.

1767. First record of glass-engraving in district.

1772. James Dovey advertising for glass-cutters here.

1774. George Ensell working Coalbournbrook glasshouse.

1777. Thomas Hill, nephew of Humfrey Batchelor, buys the two Coalbournbrook glasshouses.

1778. George Ensell awarded 'Premium' by the 'Society for the Encouragement of Arts, Manufactures and Commerce', for 'plates of glass', £50.

1780. Honeyborne & Ensell making German Sheet and Crown Glass at Moor Lane.

1783. John Hill takes expert glass-makers of the district to Waterford.

1787. Richard Bradley builds his second glasshouse at Wordsley. THE RED HOUSE.

c. 1810. The third 'Bradley' glasshouse built. WHITE HOUSE.

1827. Frederick Stuart enters the industry.

1837. Thomas Webb takes over the Platts glasshouse.

1838. The Richardsons take over Bradley's.

1847. Stevens and Williams take over at Moor Lane. Royal Society of Arts' Medal for the Richardsons.

1851. The Great Exhibition: Richardsons receive Gold Medal and royal order; potmaker Squires a diploma.

c. 1855. The Albert Glassworks built at Wordsley. ALBERT GLASSWORKS.

1855. Dennis rebuilt by Thomas Webb.

1869. Philip Pargeter at the Red House.

1873. John Northwood's 'Elgin Vase' and Engelbert Kny's 'Elgin Claret Jug'.

1876. John Northwood's 'Portland Vase'.

1878. Dennis 'Grand Prix' at Paris Exhibition.

BIBLIOGRAPHY

(S.G.T.: *Transactions of the Society of Glass Technology*)

H. S. GRAZEBROOK. *Collections for a Genealogy of the Noble Families of Henzey Tyttery and Tyzack* (Stourbridge, 1877).

R. S(IMMS). *Contributions towards a History of Glass Making and Glass Makers in Staffordshire* (Wolverhampton, 1894).

JOHN NORTHWOOD. *The Reproduction of the Portland Vase* (S.G.T., 1924).

FRANCIS BUCKLEY. *Notes on the Glasshouses of Stourbridge 1700–1830* (S.G.T., 1927).

D. N. SANDILANDS. *The Early History of Glassmaking in the Stourbridge District* (S.G.T., 1931).

R. WAKEFIELD. *Old Glasshouses of Stourbridge and Dudley* (Stour Press, 1934).

JOHN NORTHWOOD. *Stourbridge Cameo Glass* (S.G.T., 1949).

GEOFFREY W. BEARD. *Nineteenth Century Cameo Glass* (Ceramic Book Company, 1956).

H. J. HADEN. *Notes on the Stourbridge Glass Trade* (Brierley Hill Libraries and Arts Committee, 1949).

W. A. THORPE. *The Collections of Glass at the Brierley Hill Public Library* (Handlist) (Brierley Hill Libraries and Arts Committee, 1949).

Stourbridge Glass Catalogue of Loan Exhibition (Festival of Britain, 1951).

INDEX